The In-Between is Everything

by Jennifer Lilley Collins

Always look for the Joy!

Love -
Jen

Psalm 118:24

This book is dedicated to my circle.

To Mom, for your love and encouragement.
To Dad, for your strength and your example.
To Mike, my Superman, for loving me through it all.
To Kalea, for your sweet and your sassy.
To Kade, for your big heart and your big hugs.
To my friends, for lifting me up and standing beside me.
To the Women's Bible Study at Waterdam Church, for your love,
wisdom and support.
Thank you all for making my in between, my everything.

In memory of my Dad, my hero and my loudest cheerleader,
Donald E. Lilley
Your laugh. Your stories. Your determination.

May 13, 1950 – February 13, 2004

Forward by Susan Balsamo

I first saw Jen sitting criss-cross applesauce on the bench with her friends at our kids' school during pick up time. My son and her daughter were in the same class, but we had never officially met. Jen was the typical "kindergarten mom". Casual like me; minimal makeup, and simply styled hair (which I thought needed a good conditioning treatment...more on that in a minute). Sitting there, she always looked so interested in what her friends were saying, so genuinely invested in the moment. I thought to myself: I wish I had a friend like that.

We officially met a year later at our children's classmate's birthday party. We were the only school friends there, so we were drawn to conversation. We talked about our kids and our families and then she shared something very personal. She was living with cancer. The girl who seemed so interested in everyone else's life was fighting for her own every day.

That hair? It was a wig. How did I not know that?

Over the next few years, being in Jen's circle of friends would provide me a glimpse into her graceful way of handling the weight of it all. The ups and downs of doctor visits, and the roller coaster of waiting for test results as she continued to live a normal life. Her days have been filled with the highs of great test results, and the lows of "what ifs".

She never let on that she was sick.

Jen has a servant's heart. She lives her life looking for ways to make those around her more comfortable. She knows what we need before we even need it and will be the first to provide it.

5

Yes, Jen has cancer, but when I have the sniffles, a basket of teas and my favorite snacks will suddenly appear on my doorstep. Jen has cancer, but she puts together flowerpots and seedlings to take to the dialysis clinic in memory of her Dad. She drops off care packages in brightly colored bags to the local cancer center and asks the nurses to give them to those who might be struggling. Jen has cancer, yet somehow, despite the exhaustion and pain she feels, she makes her friends a priority. Being a part of her tribe means you're loved, and you will always know it.

I knew we were meant to be friends when I told her about my phobia of holes. I mentioned the inside of green pepper, explaining how the patterns of the seeds freaked me out. She immediately said "Ew! And what about the insides of a cantaloupe?"

She just gets me.

Two peas in a pod; the same kind of weirdo.

You would never know by the way we laugh and carry on that she's scared, that every day can be a struggle, that each phone call could cause either celebration or her world to spin out of control. She is a pillar of strength and faith. Cancer has given her a perspective few of us will ever experience. She lives each day to be better, do better, and to lighten someone else's load.

She writes a blog; "LifeConfetti" and has been on national radio to discuss her life and her perspective. This blog has inspired many to chase a sunset, to soak in the sounds of the beach, and to drink in their blessings. A last-minute text from Jen this past January invited her tribe to a local park to huddle together under blankets on metal bleachers to watch an amazing sunset. She inspires us to enjoy the little things.

It was Jen's calling to write this book. Cancer is a part of Jen's life, but out of it comes great blessing. Jen doesn't think she is qualified to speak on how to live a life of love and service, but God has used her as an example to do just that before pen ever met paper. Her beautiful words and the way she tells a story make you feel like you are walking this experience with her.

I wasn't there with her for some of her toughest moments you'll read about in this book, but I promise Jen all the time I will be here for the rest of them. *Grab your tissues.*

As you read this book, you will feel like you know her. Believe me, it is a coveted spot to be considered her friend; a part of her tribe. She will teach you how to recognize the ordinary as oh-so-beautiful, and to realize the small stuff is THE stuff. You will learn grace under fire, faith in the flames, and how to have a God-based heart with boundless love.

I am forever blessed to be able to sit criss-cross applesauce with my friend and to be a part of her tribe.

I love you, Jen.

Susan

Chapter One

"Lost time is never found again."
BENJAMIN FRANKLIN

After solving a green bean crisis in the kitchen, I sunk into my comfortable office chair for the first time. I never finished the staff schedule because three more kids enrolled that morning. Lisa turned up the lullaby music to drown out the preschoolers returning from outdoor play. It must have been around noon. I promised I would leave early today. I wanted to run to the party store. I had to be home by four that afternoon. A woman was dropping off catalogs for the home party I promised to host for a friend. Joann started selling candles or tote bags or decorative sporks, something like that.

I stayed up late the night before to remove the pile of papers and take-out menus from my kitchen counter. I didn't have time to clean the living room or to mop the floor. As I drove to work, I mapped out my day. If I left by two, I could get home in time to clean before Spork Lady arrived.

I answered a few phone calls, covered bathroom breaks, and almost finished the schedule when the doorbell rang. Did I forget to write a tour on the calendar? I peeked out the glass window. An older gentleman stood in the foyer.

"May I speak to the owner, please?" he asked in a voice much too big for his small stature.

A salesman. I did not have much time, but I invited him into my office. I moved a few boxes of supplies and offered him a chair. I glanced at the unfinished schedule as I sat at my desk. The lights in the center were dimmed for nap time. I finally got a good look at him. Maybe it was his salt and pepper hair, Italian looks, or big personality, but the man looked like my dad. He introduced himself as Tony Bartolo.

He told me his life story along with the list of insurance plans he offered. I listened to every word. His presence filled a void in my heart. Since my dad passed away a few years earlier, my heart was still an open wound and something about this man stopped the bleeding, if only for a few minutes.

We set up an appointment for the following week so Tony could speak with the staff. He had kind eyes and a big laugh, like my Dad. I purchased a small life insurance policy that day.He was a good salesman. Knowledgeable. Caring, but not pushy. He even encouraged me to sign up for some additional supplemental insurance. I would have bought whatever he was selling.

Tony handed me the insurance documents and gathered his things. He mentioned I reminded him of his daughter. His words meant so much to me. I stuck out my hand as I said goodbye.

"I'm a hugger," he said, and then gave me a fatherly hug. I fought to hold back tears. This was silly. He put a hand on my shoulder."You're a good girl. I will see you next week." I was sad to see him go. I started to work on the schedule.

"Jen, we need you in here!" Stacy yelled from the infant room. Bella had a fever and needed to go home. By the time I called Bella's mom, finished the schedule, and opened those boxes, it was almost three.

Ugh. I didn't have time to stop at the party store. Spork Lady was coming around four. Why did I agree to this? Because it was convenient for her? It wasn't at all convenient for me. I checked with the staff and hurried to my car. My mind raced. I was always in a rush. There was never enough time. I had so much to do tonight. Clean the house. Make dinner, bath time and bedtime. Finish the report for our grant funds that was due tomorrow.

I waited as the garage door opened and I pulled in the Jeep.I jumped from the car and stopped at the inside door. Before I turned the doorknob to go inside, I closed my eyes and took a deep breath. *Round two*, I thought.

The kitchen island was littered with art projects and half-eaten bowls of goldfish crackers. Mom stood in the kitchen. I was so thankful for her. She moved in with us after Dad passed away. She was a huge help with the kids. They came to the center sometimes, but not when I worked crazy long days. Lately, it seemed they were all crazy long days. Kalea handed me a picture and Kade raised his arms. I picked him up and looked around. Cars and block towers were scattered across the family room floor and playdough snakes covered the tiny table in the morning room. Spork Lady was due in 20 minutes.

"Ok, guys. Mommy has to clean," I announced. I put Kade down and gathered the crayons and art projects from the counter.

"Why are you worried about cleaning?" Mom said. "The house is clean. It looks like kids live here."

"This place is a mess," I snapped.

I put the playdough snakes and building blocks away and swept the floor. I placed the last pillow on the couch when the doorbell rang. I opened the door to an impeccably dressed yet unfriendly woman who shoved a box at me in the doorway.

"All you need is in the box - the catalogs, the order forms, and postcard invitations," she said, shoving the box toward me. "Let me know if you have any questions. I'll see you in a couple of weeks." She turned and walked away.

I thanked her, shut the door, and avoided Mom's gaze. She never said, "I told you so", but she could have.

"Ok, let's figure out what's for dinner," I said, contemplating ordering a pizza. I walked to the kitchen, stepping over a pull toy in the hallway.

I set the box on the counter, on top of the papers I moved from the kitchen island last night. The box slid off the uneven stack of papers and knocked some magnets from the fridge. Papers cascaded like confetti in all directions. I picked up the pizza coupons, the wedding invitation, and the script for a mammogram and put them back on the fridge.

"How about chicken nuggets and mac and cheese?" I turned on the oven and put water on to boil.

"Mommy will you color with me?" Kalea asked holding the crayon box upside down, spilling them everywhere. As she climbed onto the stool, I picked up the crayons and tore a piece of paper from her tablet.

"Mommy is making dinner, Sweet Pea. Sit here and draw me a picture while I cook," I said as I pulled the chicken nuggets from the freezer. Kade pushed a car around the kitchen island and I stepped over him for about the eighth time.

"Kade, can you please play over there while Mommy cooks dinner?" I asked. Kade put his head down and pushed his car over to the family room.

"I have to go to Baltimore tomorrow," Mike announced as he walked into the kitchen and stood at the counter.

"Tomorrow?" I asked. "I have a staff meeting. What am I going to do?"

"I have to go. What do you want me to do?".

The timer screamed that the chicken nuggets were done as I mixed the butter and milk into the mac and cheese. Mike glanced at the stove, mumbled he wasn't hungry, and went back to his office.

I watched him walk away. I was horrible at this wife and mother thing. I owned two childcare centers and was responsible for 20 employees and over 80 kids. I handled tantrums from toddlers and sometimes teachers. I stayed professional while parents yelled at me about paint spots on clothing and late fees on overdue payments. The center received no violations, a perfect inspection, last month.

But at home, I failed at everything.

I scooped mac and cheese and a handful of chicken nuggets onto the kids' favorite plates. I took a plate from the cabinet and put it back. I didn't feel like eating. Kade took a bite of mac and cheese and spilled it down the front of him onto the floor. It was a good thing I didn't mop the floor earlier. I would do it after I finished that report.

I stood at the sink while the kids ate. I needed to catch my breath and slow my thoughts. The only thing I knew to do was pray. We hadn't found a church since we moved back to Pennsylvania. I spent most weekends catching up on work but I held on to my faith. I closed my eyes and bowed my head, right over a sink full of dishes.

God, I want to be a better wife, mom, and daughter. I don't know how. The kids deserve a mom who cooks food that doesn't come from a box, who doesn't work so much. I'm stressed all the time. I promised I'd never work like my dad, sacrificing precious time and his health. I feel like I am on an amuse-

ment park ride and they won't let me off. Please. Help me jump off. I can't do this anymore. Not like this.

I wiped the tears from my eyes as I washed the dishes and wiped the counter.The kids sat at the tiny table in the morning room giggling and squishing playdough snakes together. I cringed when I saw them mixing the colors together but I didn't say anything. I joined them at their table. Startled, they looked up and smiled at me, and then at each other.

"Here, Mom. Make a snake," Kade said, handing me a clump of green playdough.

I took the playdough and rolled it between my palms until it was a long, thin snake, then dangled it in front of them before coiling it on the table.

"You're a good snake maker, Mom," said Kalea.

At least they thought I was good at something.

Chapter Two

"A man travels the world over in search of what he needs, and returns home to find it."

GEORGE MOORE

"I added petty cash to the box and checked the supply closet," I told Darcie, handing her a stack of forms. I tried to do as much as I could before I left.

"We will be fine! Don't worry. You have a great time with your family," Darcie said, taking the papers and ushering me toward the door. "Don't think about this place while you are gone. I got this."

The phone rang. We looked at each other and I dove for the phone.

"Kids Kreation. Jennifer speaking," Darcie rolled her eyes. I answered some questions and set up a tour for the following week. I wrote it on the calendar and organized the papers and files on the desk. Darcie stared at me as I stood up and put my bag over my shoulder.

"Okay. Now, get out of here before the phone rings again!" Darcie said, pushing me out of the office.

"Thank you. I appreciate this. Do you need anything else from me?"

"No. Go home. Everything will be fine."

"If you hadn't come to me about the assistant position, this trip wouldn't have happened," I said. "When I told you I wanted to hire someone at dinner that night with the guys, I didn't know you wanted to get back to work. I thought you were content staying home with the kids."

"I loved being home, but I loved being a teacher," she said. "I missed it. This will get my feet wet. Maybe one day I will go back full-time."

"Well, I would like to keep you for as long as I can, please," I said. "This means a lot. You have been such a good friend."

"Blah, blah, blah," she said laughing. "Get out of here and enjoy the beach."

"Okay, okay. I'm going," I said, gathering my things. "Remember if you need anything, Allie is available. She keeps everything running smoothly over at the other center. Call her if you have any questions." I took a step out the door, stopped, and turned around. "You can call me too. I will have my phone on me."

Darcie pointed to the door. "Go! Get out of here."

* *

After a great day at the beach, Darcie texted Friday evening the center was closed and all went well. I sighed so loudly I startled Mike from his beach nap. Now I could relax for the rest of the weekend. We packed the beach gear and headed to our condo to clean up before dinner. We promised the kids pizza and a night on the boardwalk.

The pizza at The Dough Roller was the best and it was an Ocean City tradition. The carousel horse in the middle of the restaurant and the vintage lunch boxes displayed along the walls reminded me of my childhood. We were pleased to find there was no wait. The kids leaped into the booth and looked at the menu.

"Can I get one of those pink drinks, Mom?" Kalea asked, pointing to the picture of the Shirley Temple.

"Sure, Sweet Pea. Get what you want." Kalea beamed that infectious smile. She was going to be seven in a few months but when I looked at her, I still saw my baby girl.

We ordered a pepperoni pizza and spaghetti "with butter, not sauce" for Kade. He played with a matchbox car, pushing it between the salt and pepper shakers. He was going to kindergarten in the fall but I tried not to think about that. How could he be turning six?

Mike and the kids discussed what to ride first at Jolly Rogers

Amusement Park. They debated whether they wanted funnel cake or snow cones, or both. Kade had butter all over him as he ate the long spaghetti noodles with a fork. He refused to let me cut it. Kalea pulled the cheese off her pizza to eat the crust first like always. She stuck her whole hand into the glass to rescue a cherry that escaped from the toothpick. Mike sprinkled more red pepper flakes on his pizza, and set the container on the pizza server, spilling red pepper flakes all over the table. The kids giggled. I cleaned up the mess, and handed Kalea a wipe for her pink hands.

My whole world sat in that red booth. I loved the sticky fingers, the butter face, and the pepper-flaked table. Why did I have to drive 6 ½ hours to see it? The kids were growing up so fast. Mom-guilt tugged on my heart. Mike wiped the butter from Kade's face and hands.

"Kade, you will slip right off the amusement park rides with all that butter on you," Mike joked and the kids giggled.

Mike is such a good Dad. He worked hard too, but he knew how to have fun. He spent the day digging a moat in the sand with Kade's oversized dump trucks and bulldozers. He had to be exhausted but was still ready to have a good time. He was so much better at that than me.

"Mom! ...Mommy!" Kalea said, waving her hand, interrupting my thoughts. "Can we go to the pool tonight?"

"If we get back in time after the boardwalk," I said, but thinking it might be too late.

"Yay!" both kids squealed at the same time. Mike joined in, arms in the air, "Night swim!"

"Huddle together," I said, picking up my phone to take a picture. I wished I could have frozen time right there in the middle of the red pepper flakes and a pile of butter-soaked napkins.

I missed this.

God, thank you for this trip. Thank you for Darcie. Thank you for this time. I have been missing out on so much. Forgive me for taking them for granted. Big changes are coming when we get home. Thank you for opening my eyes.

"Mom," said Kade, tapping me on the shoulder. "Let's go to the boardwalk."

After a super fun night riding bumper cars and caterpillar coasters, we made it home before the pool closed. The funnel cake and snow cones fueled the kids with enough sugar to take a quick dip even though it was really late.

"These kids will be out like a light, and hopefully sleep in tomorrow," said Mike, as he put his arm around me on the way back from the pool. I couldn't remember the last time he did that. But it felt nice, and made me realize how much I missed him too.

I rested my head on his shoulder. It felt good to spend this time with Mike. We had not been on the same page for a while. He worked hard as a civil engineer for a small firm out of Washington, DC. Mike spent evenings and weekends single-handedly remodeling both centers when I took over the spaces. He painted. He put up drywall. He turned an ugly support pole into a decorative tree. He literally made my dreams come true.

I knew he loved me and I loved him, but there was a disconnect. I felt it. I knew he did too. We both worked too much and wanted to be good parents. We poured whatever energy was left at the end of the day into the kids. There was nothing left for each other.

I missed him. I missed us.

When I met Mike, I had just ended a long-term relationship. I was 25 years old and single for the first time in my adult life. I felt betrayed. Devastated. My heart was broken and I didn't want another relationship for a very long time, if ever. After I stopped crying and listening to sad music, I pulled myself together. I spent time with friends and my family. I learned how to rollerblade, took kickboxing classes at the gym, and met a group of writers who wanted to resurrect an old local newspaper. I hiked to the Cross at Jumonville and spent a lot of time at Ohiopyle, a state park in Western Pennsylvania. It was there on my 'thinking rock' that I proclaimed I was going to stay single for a solid year. Have fun, learn new things, and figure out who I was.

Wilma, my friend and co-worker, invited me to a gathering on July 3, 1998, the night before her family's 4th of July reunion picnic. I didn't want to go. I planned to go to the movies with friends from the newspaper group. Wilma was in the middle of a divorce and the reunion was for her ex-husband's family. She needed moral support. I reluctantly agreed. When she mentioned her 'very successful, very handsome' nephew, I assured her I wasn't interested. I agreed to go because she was my friend. Living in a small town, the definition of family was loose. My parents often attended Wilma's family reunion.

I had been there before. My parents were going as well.

We met in the tavern at the local fire hall. Wilma and I sat with her son Jason and some relatives at a large round table. I spent the night talking to Jason while Wilma visited with the others. More arrived as the evening went on and more chairs were pulled around the table. I was ready to call it a night when three younger guys walked in, stopping to greet a few men from our group at the pool tables. I noticed the tall guy in the ball cap first.

A few moments later, they came to the table and chairs were shuffled around to make room for them. Wilma introduced everyone quickly. I said, "hi" and they did too. The guy in the ball cap was her nephew and he was handsome. He greeted his brothers and relatives before sitting down. He looked up and I looked away, afraid I had been staring at him. My stomach was doing flip flops. Even if I had the nerve, I couldn't have talked to him in front of that boisterous group.

Wilma got a phone call and walked away from the table.

"I have to go!", she said, returning to the table for her purse. She was meeting a friend. I stood up to go with her. She was my ride.

"Oh no, Jen. I don't have time to take you home. You stay here and keep visiting."

"No," I said."I'll go home with you. It will take you a minute to drive me home."

"Mike will take you home," she said and yelled across the table. "Can you take her home?" I was horrified.

He stammered and said he couldn't. I was humiliated, rejected from a date I didn't request. He explained he took a softball to the throat the night before at a game. He spent the night in the hospital. His friends drove his Jeep to Pennsylvania because he was on pain meds and not allowed to drive. That didn't stop Wilma.

"Then you can walk her home. She lives down the street," said Wilma, pointing in the general direction.

Wilma put him on the spot. He agreed, but I wanted to crawl under the table. Wilma was anything but subtle, waving and smiling at me as she walked out the door.

Mike and I engaged in an awkward conversation for as long as we could. It was getting late and he asked if I was ready to go. As he walked me home, we talked about rollerblading and softball. Before he left, he asked if I would be at the picnic the next day.

I was suddenly looking forward to it.

I took extra time getting ready for the picnic and even arrived earlier than planned. Mike ignored me. He played horseshoes and volleyball with his friends. I sat with my Mom and Dad and visited with the other guests. I had to leave around five to go downtown to watch the fireworks with my friend Heidi. We were meeting some of her college friends. About fifteen minutes before I had to go, Mike finally came over and talked to me. I hoped we could make plans to do something the next day or at least exchange phone numbers.

"Bye. Nice meeting you," he said waving at me as I prepared to leave.

I got nothing.

Ugh. I really liked him. I asked Wilma to walk with me to my car. I wrote my phone number on a piece of paper, maybe even a gum wrapper, I found in my car and asked her to give it to him. I never made the first move. I swore off guys for a year. What was I doing?

But later that night, as we sat on the Fort Pitt Bridge, my crappy car starting to overheat in traffic, Mike called. I felt like I was fifteen again when I answered the phone. We made plans to go to Ohiopyle the following day. I must have had a big goofy grin on my face when I hung up the phone. My friend Heidi, who was salty because she was having relationship problems of her own, rolled her eyes.

"Great!" she grumbled. "I am over here dealing with boy problems, and you find Superman".

Superman. I still called him that.

We had an amazing afternoon hiking, watching the falls, and sitting on my 'thinking rock" at Ohiopyle. He left that night to go back to Virginia but he sent me flowers at work the next day. He skipped a softball game the following weekend to drive back to Pennsylvania. The gravity of that gesture was lost on me at the time. Seven months later, I relocated to Alexandria, Virginia and a year later we were married. He told me once he never thought he would get married, but he excelled at being a husband. Mike rode in on a red Jeep and rescued me back then when I didn't know I needed rescuing.

He really was my Superman.

After we put the kids to bed, we sat on the balcony, looking out over the water. The ocean breeze felt good on our sun-tinged skin. Mike turned on some music but then turned it off to listen to the waves. We sat in silence, taking the ocean air into our lungs. It was healing. Mike took my hand. I smiled and held on tight.

"I'm having the best weekend," I said, breaking the silence. "I have been so wrapped up in the center. I needed this break."

"Yes, your staff can handle things when you aren't there," said Mike. "Now that you have Darcie, maybe you can free yourself up a little more."

"Maybe we don't go back," I said, only half-joking.

Something about the ocean calmed me and brought me peace. I imagined my worries crashing into the shore and then drifting out to sea. I closed my eyes and let the air dance across my face. When I opened my eyes, the moon appeared from behind the clouds. It was so bright. Its light skipped across the water to shore like a pathway inviting me into the heavens. I considered the invitation. Mike said he was going to bed. I took one last look at the moon and another deep breath of the ocean air. Then I shut the sliding glass door behind me.

When I woke up, everyone was still sleeping. I pulled my clothes from my suitcase and jumped in the shower. I checked out the white stripes on my shoulders and noticed the pink burn from yesterday turned to tan and didn't hurt anymore. I laughed because I looked like I was wearing a white bathing suit. I noticed my left breast looked different. That was when I found it.

The lump. Panic came over me as I felt it again. It was definitely there. I swallowed hard, and put it out of my mind. Nothing was messing up this trip.

I didn't say anything to Mike. I fidgeted with my bathing suit all day, checking to see if the lump was still there. I chased waves with the kids. I filled buckets of water for the sand fort. I focused on them. I didn't want to think about the lump or the pending doom I felt in the pit of my stomach. As the kids worked on their fort, I sat under the umbrella. I listened to their squeals and giggles carry over the crashing waves. I realized I was crying. I turned into the ocean breeze to dry my tears.

God, I am scared. What is this? This trip opened my eyes to what I had been missing. It has been forever since I had such a great time. Is this our last trip to the beach? What is that lump? Please don't let it be cancer. Please don't let me be sick.

"Mom, look!" said Kade, standing up to his waist in the sand. "We are going to dig to the other side of the earth!"

I looked at his big goofy grin. He was covered in sunscreen, sand, and pure joy.

"Well, you better keep digging then," I said, and picked up a shovel.

I refused to let the "what-ifs" derail my weekend. I would figure this all out when we got home. We spent the rest of the weekend soaking in the sun and spending much needed time together. I pretended everything was alright, but I hugged them all a little tighter. Time might be slipping away from me sooner than I thought, but I was digging in my heels.

On Tuesday morning, I was missing the beach as I caught up at the center after two days away. Things were fine. There were no catastrophes, no emergencies, just a list of messages to return and papers to file. I had one more week of summer break with the kids and I wanted to spend some time with them. I needed to schedule a mammogram. The phone rang. I jumped and answered it on the first ring.

"Jennifer!" I heard Tony say on the other line. "I just stopped by your center and they told me you had a new location. Congratulations!"

It was Tony, the insurance guy. He stopped in from time to time when he was in the area.

I was sitting at my desk when Darcie arrived.

"Welcome back! How was the trip?"

I looked up at her smiling face and said, "It was amazing," and burst into tears.

"What's wrong?" Darcie asked, shutting the office door behind her.

I hadn't told anyone I found the lump. I kept that to myself for two days. She listened as I unloaded all of it, and sat next to me while I made the appointment for my first mammogram. They couldn't get me in until Friday morning, August 31st, the following week. It was further out than I expected but the kids would be in school by then. I begged Darcie not to tell anyone. I hadn't even told Mike yet. Darcie agreed to keep it to herself, but encouraged me to talk to Mike. She told me to go home and spend the afternoon with the kids.

"It's going to be okay, Jen," Darcie said as she gave me a hug. "I will be here for you, whatever you need. You can trust me."

Chapter Three

"You'll have bad times, but it'll always wake you up to the good stuff you weren't paying attention to."

ROBIN WILLIAMS, GOOD WILL HUNTING

I typed the words and hesitated before I hit send.

"I have something to tell you, but I have chickened out all weekend. Can we talk when you get home?" I texted Mike. No turning back now.

So many times over the last week, I tried to tell Mike, but I couldn't find the words. Mike went to a Pirates game with a friend. If I texted him, I couldn't back out when he got home. I put the kids to bed and loaded the dishwasher. I was folding laundry when I heard my phone beep.

"Scaring me. But yes. We can talk," Mike texted back.

I had to do it. Tonight. It was late, but I mopped the floor, putting my nervous energy to good use. I moved a load of laundry to the dryer.I turned on the television in the bedroom to check the game. It was the top of the 7th inning. He was going to be later than he thought. Maybe I could just tell him tomorrow.

I just dozed off when I heard the chime of the front door. I heard his footsteps move toward the office and his keys hit his desk. The office chair squeaked as he sat down to check for late day emails and turn off his computer. He came up the steps and opened the door. He went into the bathroom while I pretended to sleep. My heart was beating fast. He crawled into bed. When I didn't move, he put his hand on my shoulder.

"What's going on?" he asked.

I turned to face him, thankful that our room was so dark at night. I opened my mouth but the words didn't come. Only tears. He hugged me.

"Tell me," he said.

I took a deep breath and let it all out. He held me and let me cry. He asked why I hadn't told him sooner. I wasn't sure. I didn't tell him I told Darcie.

"It is going to be okay. I will take Friday morning off. It could be a lot of things. Let's not worry until we know more," he said with reassuring confidence. Mike was always the reasonable one, the thinker, the fixer. I cried until I fell asleep. I slept better that night than I had in a week.

A couple days later, I came home early from work and Mike asked me to go to lunch, just us. We were spending more time together. As we sat at the table, the conversation stopped and we both grew quiet. I knew it was on his mind too.

"I'm nervous," I said. "I researched online and most lumps are not breast cancer. It could be a cyst or other things. I am hoping it is nothing."

"See? You are going to be fine," said Mike, taking my hands, "You are."

"I hope so. I just keep thinking about it. I don't want to go through chemo and lose my hair. I don't want to wear a scarf. I don't want to carry around a bucket in case I get sick. I don't want the kids to see me like that..."

"Stop worrying about that stuff. I don't want you to have to go through all of that either. Let's see what they say. It's going to be okay." I prayed he was right.

On Friday, we sat in the waiting room, cracking jokes and looking at magazines. An older couple bickered in the hallway.

"That will be us one day," Mike said. I wondered if we would grow old together.

A very friendly nurse named Margaret handed me a bunch of forms. After I filled out the paperwork, she took me to the locker room to change, chatting the whole time.

"Can I have your prescription please?" she asked. I dug through my purse. The prescription hung from a clip on my refrigerator for the last nine months.

When she realized I found a lump, she explained I needed a prescription for a diagnostic mammogram, not a baseline mammogram.

"I'll take care of it. Don't worry. I'll be back in a few minutes," Margaret said with a big smile, whistling as she walked down the hall.

I sat on the chair and looked at the medical pictures of breasts on the wall. I had no idea there was so much inside of them. I imagined someone going through a catalog choosing just the right picture to display on these beige walls. Which ones would really brighten up the space? What poor handyman had to hang those pictures? Were there catalogs of pictures like that? Were they organized by body part? Who drew these pictures? I pictured a starving artist receiving the assignment to draw the interior workings of a breast or an ear canal.

Margaret knocked on the door and told me they were working on my prescription. After she told me a funny story about her neighbor, she asked me to remove my robe. I was embarrassed and really cold, but did as she asked. As she examined the lump, her bright eyes and cheery attitude dimmed. She became more professional. Something was wrong.

The tears began to fall as Margaret instructed me how to position myself for the exam. Ignoring my tears and all eye contact, Margaret stepped behind the counter and took the first picture. An image flashed on the computer screen. When Margaret saw me looking at it, she tilted the screen so I couldn't see it. She repositioned me to take more pictures.

"Can you see anything?" I asked. "Is everything okay?"

Margaret didn't answer. I knew her silence meant bad news. She escorted me to another room to wait while the doctor viewed the images. I was freezing in the air-conditioned room and pulled the thin gown around me. *Ellen* was on the television. A few moments later, Margaret returned to tell me the doctor ordered a sonogram. She handed me a box of tissues and went to get Mike.

Another woman walked into the waiting area and I watched television as though nothing was wrong. The door opened again and Mike

27

appeared. He was relaxed, unaware there was a problem until he saw me crying. Margaret explained I was waiting for an additional test. Mike sat down beside me, but I couldn't speak. He held my hand while I continued to cry.

A moment later, a technician took me back for the sonogram. She was pleasant but quiet. As she moved the wand, I looked at the computer screen but I didn't know what the pictures meant. I heard a clicking noise. She must have seen the worry on my face.

"I am just taking measurements", she said, never taking her eyes from the screen.

Another technician entered the room carrying a file folder with small images clipped to the front. The two of them spoke but I couldn't hear them.

More clicking.

"I don't see anything," one of them said. That gave me a glimmer of hope. Maybe it was nothing after all. The second technician left.

"What's going on?" I asked, with no response.

A minute later, a small, dark-haired woman came into the room. She was wearing a white coat so I assumed she was a doctor. She didn't introduce herself. She was angry and annoyed.

"What is the problem?" she said, glaring at the technician. She did not address me but took the wand and moved it around roughly as she stared at the screen.

"I don't see anything here," she muttered to herself.

That little glimmer of hope grew bigger.

She looked me in the eyes for the first time and with no emotion, said, "You have a suspicious mass. Most likely cancer. It will have to be removed. You'll have to call a breast surgeon."

I stared at her, speechless, processing her words. Before I could reply, she put down the wand, picked up some files, and walked out the door. The two technicians looked at each other. Horrified, one of them handed me some pamphlets from the counter while the other technician went to get Mike.

As I joined Mike in the waiting room, Margaret burst through the door.

"We have wonderful doctors here and they are going to take good care of you," she said, handing me a folder of information. I couldn't speak. Margaret looked like she was going to say more, but she hugged me instead. I held onto her tightly before muttering a quick goodbye.

Mike took my hand as we walked to the car. It was a sunny August day but I wished it was raining. It was unfair such a bad thing could happen on a beautiful day.

"I have cancer," I said. The words sounded foreign coming out of my mouth.

Mike stopped short, squeezing my hand. "They didn't say that."

"Yes, they did. I have to see a breast surgeon. I have cancer."

We rode in silence on the way to lunch. Why was the sky so blue? And those clouds so white and puffy? Again, I wished for rain.

I held back tears in the booth as we pretended to eat. A couple of kids ran up and down the aisles. A group of older gentlemen laughed as they ate at the counter bar. A large party of women cackled at a nearby table. I was jealous. For them, it was an ordinary day. Everything was right in their world. My world was imploding.

"You are going to beat this thing," Mike said. "Everything is going to be okay."

There wasn't a bit of doubt in his voice. We left the restaurant, our plates full, our souls depleted.

On the way home, I checked off the ingredients in my head. I had them all, even the chocolate chips. I had everything I needed and enough time to bake cookies for the kids before they got home from school. I had an urge to bake chocolate chip cookies.

When I got in the door, I set the butter on the counter to soften and glanced at the clock. I had time to rest for a little while. I walked upstairs to the bedroom. Mike followed me. I threw the decorative pillows on the floor and we collapsed on the bed. I buried my head in his shoulder and sobbed.

This couldn't be real. This wasn't happening...but it was. I had cancer.

Mike held me tight, like he tried to hug the hurt out of me. My head was buried in his chest. I felt his hand go from my back to his face, and then he squeezed tighter. He was crying too. I felt his love wrapped around me. As much as he wanted to, he couldn't make this go away.

When that doctor said I had cancer, everything changed. I was overcome with questions and fears. Was I going to die? Who would take care of my children? How much time did I have? I squeezed Mike tighter as the sobs kept coming. What about him? I didn't want Mike to have to raise the kids on his own? I was terrified. I felt cheated and robbed. Mike and I tried for years to have children. They were only 5 and 6 years old! Was that all the time I would get with the children I prayed for?

God, why would you bless me with children and then call me home? Was this some kind of cruel joke? Did I deserve this for working too much? For having messed up priorities? I finally made a decision at the beach to make some changes? Was I too late? God, I need to be okay. I want to be here to raise my kids, to grow old with Mike. I need this to be okay. I am not strong enough to do this!!

Maybe I had no more tears to cry, or God heard my prayers. I felt peace. God would walk me through this, but I had to make some changes. Now. I let the world steal me away from what mattered. My life was a checklist of things to get done, my only focus to add the checkmark next to the task. I rushed the kids through dinner to wash the dishes. I denied them a second bedtime story to finish that report. All I ever wanted was to be a mom, but I didn't deserve the title.

My days were long and my patience was thin. I poured myself into work when I should have poured myself into them. Even when we did all the fun things, my mind was steps ahead, preparing for the next activity. Never fully present. I missed so much, but no more. I would show my kids I could be a better mom.

I had to bake chocolate chip cookies.

The bus was coming soon. I dried my tears and wiped my face. I went downstairs and pulled out the mixer. I poured all my energy and all my love into that special batch of cookies. With every scoop of flour, with every beaten egg; I relived all the special moments of my kids' lives –the days they were born, the holiday celebrations, vacations, the everyday moments. My mind overflowed with flashes of happy memories, and I grieved the moments that passed when I wasn't paying attention. So many moments. *Why didn't I pay attention?*

The cookies baked and the house filled with the scent of chocolate, childhood, and a mother's love. As I lifted each warm, gooey cookie from the pan, I promised things would be different. No more rushing through life to get to the next thing. Not one more moment taken for granted. As the cookies cooled on the counter, I decided the rest of my life, whatever that meant, started now.

Mike came into the kitchen to tell me it was time for the bus. We stood on the front stoop and waited for the kids. I heard the roar of the engine coming up the hill. As the bus went by, I saw the kids' faces in the windows, smiling and waving. I had never been so excited to see them.

Kade came down the sidewalk first, his blue backpack bobbing behind him with each quick step, a big goofy grin on his face.

"You're home, Mom! I didn't know you would be here!" he said. I hugged him and kissed the top of his head. Kalea came behind him, her pink backpack securely resting on her shoulders. I hugged her but she ran in the house before I could kiss her after Mike yelled, "Who wants cookies?"

The kids climbed up on the counter stools. Their eyes grew big as they looked at the freshly baked cookies. Within seconds, chocolate dripped down Kade's chin onto his new school clothes. I grabbed a napkin. With the next bite the chocolate dripped down his arm.

"These are the best cookies ever, Mommy!" said Kade, "Can you make these every day when we come home from school?"

We all laughed at the sight of Kade, chocolate all over him. Mike told the kids not to eat too many cookies because we were going out for dinner to kick off the long holiday weekend. Because it was late in the afternoon on a Friday before Labor Day, the surgeon's office was closed. I would have to wait until Tuesday to make an appointment.

Mike hung out with the kids and I went upstairs to get ready. I grabbed my phone and sat on the bed. I didn't want anyone else to know yet, but I had to tell Darcie and Allie. I would have a lot of appointments very soon. I wasn't up for a phone conversation, and as inappropriate as it might have been, I texted them both.

A few moments later, both Allie and Darcie texted me back messages of support. They would do whatever I needed. I was grateful for them both. I was used to handling everything on my own. I was the person who always helped everyone else. I was going to need help this time.

Chapter Four

"Don't do that chemo stuff. You can cure your own cancer with maple syrup and baking soda...or asparagus...or lemon water... or juicing..."

RANDOM PEOPLE WITH NO MEDICAL BACKGROUND

I assumed a cancer diagnosis qualified as an emergency visit, but I couldn't get an appointment with the breast surgeon for another week. The rogue cells growing in my body were not as concerning to them as they were to me. In the meantime, I googled every possible alternative outcome for what was on those images. If there was even a 0.00004% chance that it was something else, I prayed it would be.

After a nurse named Caroline took my vitals, Mike and I sat in the small exam room and waited for Dr. Barton. Our nerves so frazzled, we jumped at the quiet knock on the door. Dr. Barton was a stylish woman with jet-black hair wearing jeans, boots, and a pretty pastel blouse under her white lab coat. She was confident and friendly and looked like she could play a doctor on television.

"Hello there, my name is Dr. Barton," she introduced herself, extending her hand to both of us. "I am not going to waste your time here. It is what it is. We know it is cancer, so I want to move forward as quickly as possible."

My heart sank. Tears welled up in my eyes but I held them back. I knew if I lost it, there was no turning back. I felt Mike's hand on my shoulder.

"Let's send you down for a biopsy and then we can come back

here and talk," she said. "I'll call them. Caroline will walk you down there."

She shut the door behind her. A few moments later, Caroline returned and asked me to sign more paperwork. She walked us downstairs to another waiting room, where they handed me another clipboard of forms. I only finished the front of the first page when they called me back for blood work.

I told the phlebotomist I hadn't finished the forms. She shrugged and told me I could finish when she was done. It was September but the woman wore a thick handknit cardigan with cat-shaped buttons. It was really cold in the hospital though. She also wore a necklace that said, "Cat Lady". She asked me to verify my name and birthdate and then wrapped a rubber tourniquet around my arm.

"So what are you here for today?", she asked to distract me from the pinch of the needle. When I whispered the words "breast cancer," she stiffened, covered the injection site with a cotton ball and removed the needle.

"I am an involuntary member of that club too," Cat Lady said, placing a bandaid over the cotton ball. "You will get through this. Hang in there."

I teared up and she handed me a tissue. "This may sound crazy but one day—not right now—but one day, you will realize this is a gift. There will be blessings in the storm."

I smiled, but I wanted to punch her in the throat. *A gift? A blessing in the storm? Give me a break!* Cat Lady patted me on the shoulder and walked me back to the waiting room. She gave me a hug.

"Good luck, sweetie. You can do this." I couldn't walk away from her fast enough. I took my seat next to Mike to finish my paperwork.

"Jennifer!" a voice screamed from the other side of the room. I handed the technician the clipboard and followed her into another beige room. She pulled a gown from a drawer and left. As I changed, I looked around. At least this room had pictures of an old porch and not another body part.

A few moments later, two women entered and the blond one prepared a syringe. The brunette warned me the numbing medicine would feel like a bee sting. I braced myself as the blond nurse said, "Little pinch." I never felt a thing.

The samples of the tumor would determine the type of breast cancer and the type of treatment. I didn't realize there were 'types' of breast cancer. I thought the type was breast cancer. The brunette warned the instrument sounded like a cap gun as she prepared for the procedure.

"Ready?" the brunette said. "One, two, three..." and then I heard a pop. It sounded and felt like a shotgun, not a cap gun. I jumped and let out a yelp.

"Did you feel that?" they both asked in unison.

"Yes! It felt like you shot me."

"Let's give you another dose of numbing medicine," the blond one said, grabbing another syringe. "Here comes the bee sting," she warned again. I still didn't feel a thing. They waited another few minutes before resuming.

"One, two, three..." the brunette counted down, then I heard another pop and felt like a gunshot victim again.

"Honey, if you felt that, this numbing medicine is not working. We can send you down to Emergency and have them put you under." I didn't want to go to the emergency room. That might take forever. The kids would be home from school soon. My mom didn't even know I was there.

"How many times do you have to do it?" I asked.

"Your doctor ordered seven specimens, so we need to do it five more times."

"Just do it," I said, "I can get through five more times." The blond and the brunette looked at each other.

"You sure? I know it hurts. You don't have to put yourself through this," the blond one pleaded. "We can send you down right now to get this done, pain-free."

"No, I can handle it. Five more times. I can do this." I closed my eyes and prepared for five more shotgun blasts.

When I was three, my dad was in a car accident, hit by a drunk driver. I remembered that night clearly. My mom, my brother and I were waiting for Dad to come home so we could go out to dinner. It was getting later and later. There was a knock at the door. I stood at my mom's feet as she talked to the big man in the black raincoat on the porch. I didn't understand what happened but my neighbor came over and put us to bed. When I woke up, my grandma was at our house but my mom wasn't home. I found out when I was older that my dad almost didn't make it. He suffered broken bones and serious internal injuries. He was in the hospital a long time and then home for a while before he was able to go back to work. The accident left his kidneys damaged and when he developed high blood pressure, the medications he was prescribed further compromised them. Dad was a hard worker. He let the stress of his job affect his mood and his health. He suffered his first heart attack in his mid-40s. The heart and kidney problems grew worse. After several heart attacks and bypass surgery, Dad was forced to slow down. He took a job that was less demanding and made some lifestyle changes.

When I was in college, my parents bought an old house they want- ed to renovate. Days after they closed on the property, Dad received a phone call from his doctor. His bloodwork showed extremely high levels of potassium which indicated a serious problem. He went to the hospital and received emergency dialysis. He was diagnosed with renal failure and started dialysis three days a week. An AV fistula, a proce- dure that connects an artery and a vein for easier access during dial- ysis, was placed in his arm. Oftentimes, that fistula would not work. He had to go to the hospital to have a temporary shunt placed near his collarbone so he could have dialysis until they repaired the fistula. One time, he could not be placed under anesthesia due to related health problems. The doctors had to decide what to do because he needed dialysis.

"Just do it," he said, interrupting the doctor's discussion. The procedure was a fairly quick one and only required a one-inch inci- sion so Dad told them to do it without anesthesia. He assured them he could handle it. He lay on a hospital bed as they cut through his skin, inserted the shunt, and stitched him up, all with no pain medication. He yelled and squeezed the bed rail, but he got through it.

"Jenny, sometimes you gotta do what you got to do," he told me as he shared the story.

I "got to do" this. My dad was the strongest man I knew and I was his daughter. That strong Lilley blood ran through my veins too. I could get through this, just like he did.

"Just do it."

"Alright, you ready for the next one?" asked the brunette. I nodded, closed my eyes, and squeezed the bed rail.

"One, two, three…" she counted. I heard the pop and felt the metal blast deep into my skin to retrieve another piece of the tumor eating me from the inside out.

"Take that," I thought, imagining the tumor screaming in agony as it took the hit. That vision was the distraction I needed to soften the blows. If this was what it took to get rid of this cancer, then so be it.

Three down, four more to go.

As the brunette started the "One, two, three…" count, I interrupted her, "Please stop counting down. That makes it worse. Just do it."

The blond nurse nodded and winced as she prepared for the fourth attack. She was uncomfortable doing the procedure without the local anesthesia. The brunette offered her hand for me to squeeze. When I looked at her hesitantly, she said, "I was a labor and delivery nurse for years. You can't hurt me. Let's do this!"

I took her hand and squeezed through the fifth, sixth, and then the final shot.

When it was over, I was sweating and nauseous from the pain. The blond nurse handed me an ice pack, rubbed my arm, and looked at me with those eyes, those pitiful eyes that made me feel like a sick person.

"You take a moment. We will process these samples and will be back to get you out of here."

I sat in the room alone, taking deep breaths through the throbbing pain. I remembered all those procedures Dad had over the years. Not the big surgeries, but the countless outpatient procedures that he endured. All those times I sat in the waiting room, reading a book and watching the time, thankful when it was a quick procedure so I could get home or back to work. Dad always walked out looking a little tired, a little beat up, but he always had a smile on his face. I saw him go in and I saw him come out, but until now, I never thought much about what happened down the hall. I was ashamed that I didn't know, that I didn't understand the pain and the discomfort he must have felt. I knew he did that to protect me. He didn't want me to know what he had been through.

Now I did.

"I'm sorry, Dad," I whispered. "I didn't know."

In the cold, sterile room, the only noise was the low hum of the air conditioner and the ticking of the clock that hung on the wall in front of me. I watched the second hand move around the numbers. How many rotations I let slip by without notice.

"Okay," the blond said, opening the door, "Dr. Barton will see you now."

Dr. Barton sat at her desk and explained my diagnosis as best she could with what she knew so far. Mike listened intently. I heard the important words.

Stage two based on size... will know more after further testing... doesn't look like any lymph node involvement... chemotherapy... surgery... maybe or maybe not radiation...medication for five years... treatment will take about a year... good chance for survival... referral for an oncologist... set you up for more testing.

It was a lot to digest. As she walked us to the door, she handed me a card for an oncologist named Dr. Mendez.

"He's good, young. You'll like him," she said. "Give him a call."

On the drive home, we didn't say much. I looked at the sky. It was blue. Puffy-white- clouds hung in the heavens, mocking me. Another beautiful day spent in a medical office. I pulled down the sun visor to block my view and ripped the hospital bracelet off my wrist. We beat the kids home. I wanted to get dinner started and Mike needed to get to work.

"I'm going to have to work most of the night," Mike said. "You okay?"

"I'm sorry," I said. "I had no idea it was going to take so long today." Mike worked hard already. This wasn't fair to him either.

"It's okay," Mike said, hugging me gently and kissing my forehead before heading to his office. "Take it easy."

I browned the meat and added the tomato sauce and seasonings for our spaghetti dinner, and I heard the bus outside. The kids ran inside, dropping backpacks and lunchboxes at the door. Kalea gave me a hug, and I winced as she pressed against me. I was still so sore.

"Ooooooh, brownies," Kade squealed with delight, standing on tip-toes to look at the pan. I made them before we left this morning. "Can I have one?"

"After dinner. I got ice cream too!"

Chapter Five

"Into each life some rain must fall, some days be dark and dreary."

HENRY WADSWORTH LONGFELLOW

The next day at work, I filled in Darcie and Allie on everything, but the rest of the staff still didn't know. I wasn't ready to tell them. I hadn't even told my mom. I would wait until I knew more. Dr. Barton said I had to have a series of tests before I could start treatment.

A few weeks later, Mike made plans for a night away in Erie to celebrate our 12th wedding anniversary. I wasn't feeling much like celebrating, but Mike insisted. We planned to arrive Friday afternoon, spend some time near the water, and have a nice dinner. Mike told me to pack a dress. We were going to a fancy restaurant. Saturday we would go to Presque Isle Park. He knew how much I loved to be near the water. It was September, so we imagined a beautiful day, not quite warm enough to get in the water but the perfect day to sit on a blanket on the beach.

That Friday, Mike was fighting a cold and a fast-approaching deadline. We left later than planned. Mike came downstairs with his bags and did not look well. His cheeks were flushed and his eyes were glassy.

"You sure you are up for this trip?" I asked. "I am okay with re-scheduling after all this mess is over."

"No, I'll be fine. I will take some medicine. We are going to celebrate our anniversary," he insisted. I grabbed some medicine, cough drops, and a box of tissues and put them in my bag.

It rained the whole way to Erie and harder as we pulled into the parking lot of our hotel. By the time we got to the room, we were drenched and Mike was shivering. I felt his head.

"You have a fever," I said. "We should have just stayed home."

"I'll take some medicine and I'll be fine in a little bit. We can rest before dinner," he said collapsing on the bed.

I was okay with the rain. Although he refused my offer to order in, Mike agreed to eat a casual dinner in the hotel restaurant. We were back in the room by 8pm. Mike went to bed and I sat up worrying about what was to come.

In the morning, the skies were dark gray and the rain continued. Mike was feeling better and wanted to salvage as much of the trip as possible.

"Let's drive through the park. Maybe the rain will stop and we can sit on the beach for a while and find something to do."

By the time we left the hotel, the skies were less gray and the rain had slowed to a drizzle. I told him we could just go home, but he kept driving. He was determined. Just before we arrived, the rain stopped. Mike parked the car and grabbed a blanket from the back.

"Let's go. Just for a while," he said.

As soon as we got out of the car, the cold wind coming off the lake assaulted our faces. Mike grabbed my hand and we pressed on toward the beach. He attempted to spread out the blanket, but the wind tossed it around until he gave up. He folded the blanket and plopped down before the wind could take it again. He patted his hand on the blanket, and I took a seat beside him. He put his arm around me and I snuggled close to him.

"Sorry this was such a crappy anniversary," Mike said. "But Happy Anniversary!"

"Happy Anniversary!" I said. "It's okay. I don't feel much like celebrating right now."

"I know," Mike said, pulling me closer.

"Maybe we can come back for our anniversary next year? I should be done with chemo and surgery and maybe I will have some hair. A total redo?"

"It's a deal. You ready to go, then?"

"Yes! Let's get out of here. It's freezing!"

We got home earlier than expected and took the kids for ice cream. That night, we told the kids I was sick. We didn't want to overwhelm them, but wanted to be as honest as possible. I didn't want to tell them at all but I knew it had to be done.

"Mommy went to the doctor and found out she is sick," Mike said. Both kids turned to look at me. I smiled at them, sensing their concern.

"What kind of sick?" Kalea asked.

"Mommy has cancer," I said trying to make that sound as normal as possible.

"Isn't that bad?" Kade asked. "That's what those kids on that commercial have, the kids that wear hats and have wheelchairs." Kade was always curious about the commercials for St. Jude's Hospital.

"Mommy is going to be okay," Mike said. "She has a really good doctor."

"You are right, Bud. Those kids have cancer too. There are many different kinds. My doctor is going to make me better," I said. "Okay," Kade said.

"What is going to happen?" Kalea asked. I couldn't look her in the eyes because I felt her fear settle into my heart.

"The doctors can help me get rid of the cancer but I have to take some really yucky medicine, and–."

"–Like that cough syrup I don't like?" Kade interrupted.

"Kade! Mommy was talking," Kalea scolded.

"It's okay," I said, putting my arm around Kalea. "Yes, Kade. You don't like that cough medicine but it makes you feel better, right? I am not going to like my medicine either. It will help me feel better, but it might make me really tired and sick."

"But then you will be better?" Kalea asked.

"Yes, the medicine will make me sick for a while but I will get better. The medicine will get rid of the cancer, but that medicine is so yucky it will make me lose my hair too."

"What do you mean? All of it?" Kalea said.

"Yes, but guess what?" I said. "When that happens, I get to wear a wig."

"So you won't be bald like those kids in the commercials?" Kade

41

asked.

"I will lose my hair, Bud, but I will wear a wig so I can look the same as I do now. Just until it grows back."

"It will grow back then?" Kalea asked.

"Yes. My hair will grow back and I will get better," I said. Kade got up from the couch to build blocks. Kalea snuggled against me.

"You guys will have to help Mommy if she is sick," Mike said. "Can you do that?"

"Yes," said Kade, building a tower on the floor.

"Yes," said Kalea, hugging me. "I will help you, Mommy."

"Thank you," I said. "Do you have any questions?"

"No," said Kade, focused on his blocks.

"No," said Kalea. "Can I go color a picture?"

"Sure, Sweet Pea."

She walked over to the tiny table and sat down with her crayons and paper. I slid over next to Mike and rested my head on his shoulder.

"Do you think they are okay?" I asked him, watching Kade sort his magnetic blocks by shape.

"Yes," Mike said. "They are stronger than you think."

"I hope so."

A moment later, Kalea handed me a picture. She drew a big red heart in the middle of the paper and wrote: *I love you Mommy!* at the top and: *Love, Kalea* on the bottom.

"I love it, Baby Girl," I said. "Thank you so much. You did a beautiful job."

She smiled, hesitated for a moment, and threw her arms around me. I wrapped my arms around her, placing my hand behind her head like I did when she was a baby. I held on tight, feeling her love run through me. I held onto her until she let go. I would always be the last one to let go.

* *

Later that night, I added school and sports dates to the calendar that hung on my pantry door. I flipped to October and saw "CHEMO" written on October 3rd. I looked through the rest of the year. My brother was getting married in a couple of weeks and Kade turned six later in

October. Thanksgiving was in November. Kalea turned seven in December, just a couple weeks before Christmas.

Cancer had terrible timing.

That night, after the kids went to bed, I wondered if I should reach out to a friend from high school. I didn't know her well but Christi and I connected on Facebook. I followed her posts after her breast cancer diagnosis. She was a mom of two beautiful young girls. What did I say? *Hi. We barely spoke in high school, but I saw on Facebook you had cancer. Can we talk?* I felt awkward, but I sent her a message anyway. We grew up in the same very small town, and some might have said that made us family.

My two aunts had breast cancer, but I wasn't ready for my family to know. My dad's side of the family was pretty big, and news like that traveled fast. They were coming to Chris' wedding next month. I didn't want the "sister with cancer" to put a damper on his big day. I hadn't told Chris yet either.

Christi responded right away and we made plans to talk. She told me when to order my wig, what clothes to buy, and what supplies would make me more comfortable. I knew it had to be hard to relive what she had been through. It hadn't been that long since she finished her treatment.

"I will help you however I can. I will always be honest. I will always tell you the truth," she said. I appreciated that. I wanted to know what to expect. Christi urged me to schedule an appointment at a wig salon soon since it could take weeks for delivery. I didn't want to be unprepared so I called a salon recommended by a friend that afternoon.

I arrived at the salon and the receptionist walked me to a door near her desk, down the steps to the basement. A chair, a mirror and an assortment of wigs on creepy heads filled the small room. A woman stacking heads on a shelf introduced herself as Nancy. She held an armful of creepy heads, but she couldn't have been more warm and welcoming.

"What kind of cancer do you have?" she asked.

"Breast cancer."

"Yes, you will definitely lose your hair from the chemo," she said as she grabbed some catalogs and a few heads, setting them on the counter.

"What kind of wig were you thinking? Long, short, curly, straight, what color?"

"I just want something similar to my hair," I said. "I don't want my kids to be scared."

We looked through the catalogs and Nancy tried a few on my head. I chose a wig the same color as mine but a little longer. I cut my long hair to my shoulders when I found out I had cancer, thinking losing it might be easier if it wasn't so long. I decided to have a little fun with a longer wig. I could curl it and style it like real hair.

Nancy asked about my plan for when my hair started to fall out. I didn't have one. She told me to call her when the time came and she would shave my head and help me fit my wig. I gave her a hug and left the salon feeling accomplished. I took back some control and it felt good. After weeks of feeling helpless, I was happy to check something off my list.

Christi advised me to buy yoga pants and comfortable shirts. I had a stack of gift cards Mike gave me for past birthdays and holidays in my wallet that I was too busy to spend. The next day, I bought yoga pants, t-shirts and zip up hoodies in every color they had. Those clothes didn't cost me a dime.

I was feeling better about everything. I ordered my wig. I purchased a new chemo wardrobe, and I made some long-term plans for the center. I worked with Allie and Darcie, training them to do some of the things I did, in case I wasn't able. Things were falling into place. The initial shock had gone away and I was focused on getting organized and ready. I needed a plan.

When I made my initial appointment to see Dr. Mendez, I didn't know Mike had to be out of town for work that day. Mike immediately offered to change the meeting but I told him that wasn't necessary. I could go by myself. From what I understood, I only needed to see the oncologist so he could order the necessary tests. It sounded like a formality.

"We have no idea what is coming down the road. When I start chemo and then have surgery, you might have to take a lot of time off," I said. "This is one appointment. You go to your meeting next week. I can go by myself this time." Reluctantly, he agreed. I assured him I would be fine and I would call him after to tell him everything.

* *

It was a rainy Saturday afternoon and Mike was busy working around the house. I decided to take the kids to the movies at the last minute. I swapped my crossbody for my 'big purse'. We stopped at the dollar store to pick out candy and drinks. We got a big tub of popcorn and found seats as the lights dimmed.

The first preview was for *Despicable Me 2*. The kids' eyes lit up as they giggled watching the minions dance on the screen. They loved the first movie.

"Can we see that, Mom?" Kade asked, pointing to the screen.

"Please, Mom," Kalea added.

"Absolutely!" I said, munching on a handful of popcorn. The release date flashed across the big screen and my stomach sank. Would I still be here in July of 2013?

Consumed with making doctor appointments and planning for my absence at the center, I couldn't see past the next day of work, afternoon with the kids, or test at the hospital. I didn't know what July 2013 was going to look like, or if I would still be here to see it.

I decided right then. We were going to see that movie!

The winter before our wedding, Dad had heart surgery and numerous complications. He transferred from the hospital to a rehab facility for a month to wean off the ventilator. When the tubes were finally removed, he asked the doctors if he would make it to walk me down the aisle at my wedding that September, less than seven months away.

They said, "No."

But he did. My dad walked me down the aisle at that little church in the mountains and it was one of the best days of my life. He told me a few years later what the doctors said.

"I didn't care what they said. I was going to walk you down that aisle!" he proclaimed, lightly pounding his fist on the dining room table.

I looked at my kids and then turned back to the big screen. I marked the square in my mind's calendar with the words, *Despicable Me 2*. I ate another handful of popcorn and passed out the M&Ms and

45

Mike & Ikes we smuggled into the theater in my big purse.

Thank you, God. Thank you for this day with my kids. And July 3, 2013, the day we see Despicable Me 2? A special day for sure. Keep showing me, Lord, in all these little ways that this is going to be okay. I trust You, Lord. I really do.

July 3, 2013 was also the 15th anniversary of the night Mike and I met. I pounded my fist on the armrest of my chair and reminded myself that I was my father's daughter.

* *

I packed some sandwiches and a few snacks and set them on Mike's desk.

"You don't have to do that every time I go out of town," Mike said, slinging his bag over his shoulder.

"I want you to eat. You skip lunch, then you get a headache."

"I don't know what you are talking about," Mike said with a serious look on his face. We both laughed and he gave me a hug. "Good luck tomorrow. Call me as soon as you are done." He left for Baltimore and I got a good night's sleep before my appointment the next day.

I pulled into the parking lot and noticed the sky. It was a blue-sky-and-puffy-white-clouds kind of day. They seemed to follow me around lately. Despite what was going on in my life, those days were still my favorite.

"Great day for a visit with my oncologist, right?" I thought to myself, looking down at the pavement. I couldn't believe I had an oncologist. I walked through the glass doors to the back of the building. My feet felt heavy like I walked in cement. I entered the empty elevator, pushed the number 5, and leaned against the wall.

"I can't believe I have to do this," I said out loud. The doors opened and I looked left then right. A glass door etched with the words "UPMC Cancer Center" taunted me until I had no choice but to open it and go inside. I kept my eyes straight ahead as I walked to the receptionist desk.

"Good morning! How can I help you?" greeted Lori. She had curly blond hair and a warm smile that put me at ease. Big surprise. She handed me a clipboard and told me to take a seat.

A bookshelf full of worn paperback books stood along the back wall.

An older gentleman with an oxygen tank sat at a card table working a half-completed puzzle. A water dispenser stood near a counter with a basket full of knit caps, donated by a local women's organization. A sign on the basket that said: *Free. Take One*, but I declined the offer. An older couple sat nearby laughing and holding hands as they watched *The Price is Right*. The man wore overalls and a ball cap to cover his bald head. I felt eyes on me and noticed a woman sitting across the room, her head tilted back resting against the wall. She was bald but wore bold makeup that accentuated her sunken facial features. She wore a bright pink tank top that revealed the bony protrusions of her collar-bone and shoulders. She wasn't staring at me, but was instead lost in her own thoughts. I chose a seat near the front of the room in the only row that faced away from the other patients.

My hands were shaking. I held the clipboard on my lap. I scribbled my name, address, and birthdate at the top. I fumbled through my purse to find my health insurance card and dropped it onto the floor. I stood to pick it up from under the chair. When I turned around, the woman in the pink tank top still stared in my direction. I grabbed my card and sat down, anxious to turn away from her and the other patients.

I flipped the page and tears fell onto the paper. I wiped them away but they kept coming. I stared at the word "cancer" then checked the 'yes' box with my trembling hand. I used to mindlessly check the 'no' boxes from diabetes to vertigo. When I wrote "breast cancer" my pen ripped the tear-soaked paper.

Why did I come here alone?

My phone vibrated in my purse. Mike texted.

"How is it going?"

"All is well. Filled out paperwork. Waiting to see the doctor," I texted back.

"Ok. Call me when finished. Love you."

"Jennifer?" a nurse called. I stood up and walked to the door, avoiding the woman in the pink tank top's stare.

After the nurse took my vitals and asked some questions, she left the room. I sat in a chair, head resting against the wall. I wasn't sure how long I sat there but the light clicked off and I sat in the dark. I was comfortable in the dark. Then I heard a soft knock on the door.

Dr. Mendez looked so young the show *Doogie Howser* came to mind. He had a baby face and a warm smile. He introduced himself and pulled the wheeled stool over to sit near me.

He asked some general questions and I answered them as matter-of-factly as I could, until I couldn't keep up the act anymore. The tears fell and my voice cracked. Dr. Mendez handed me a tissue and wheeled his stool a little closer.

For over an hour, he explained everything in great detail. He drew pictures of cancer cells, wrote the names of chemotherapy treatment options, and described the options for surgery. He estimated a time table of treatment and recovery, planned to schedule more tests, and would see me in a couple of weeks to discuss the results.

He laid it all out for me. It wouldn't be easy, but he gave me hope.

"All done. I loved Dr. Mendez. He has a plan. I think I can do this," I texted Mike as I left.

"I know you can."

I walked out of the cancer center, my feet much lighter. I looked up to the blue sky filled with puffy-white-clouds and let the sun warm my face.

Chapter Six

Standing in line at my local pharmacy, a day out of chemo, wearing a wig and feeling very sick, I overheard pharmacy techs discussing breast cancer.

Tech #1: *Ugh. Why do we have to put pink caps on everything? Why does breast cancer think it's better than everyone?*

Tech#2: *I know! I am so sick of breast cancer.*

I was thinking we could work on the calendars and newsletters through December. Get a head start?" I suggested to Allie during our morning phone call. I wanted to get as much done as I could, before I couldn't.

"Already finished," Allie said. "I am working ahead through March."

"Seriously? You are amazing!" I said as my voice cracked with emotion. Days at the center were winding down. Post-it notes and checklists littered my desk and I was struggling to get it all done.

Dr. Mendez first said I could continue to work at the center. At my last appointment, he changed his mind.

"I have been thinking, Jen," he said, looking down at the files in hand, avoiding eye contact. "I have some bad news."

I reached for Mike's hand. I felt sick to my stomach. Had they found something new? Was the cancer worse than they thought? Every possible bad scenario swirled in my head.

"One of my patients recently caught a simple cold. Her immune system was weak and she couldn't fight it," Dr. Mendez explained then took a deep breath. "We had to stop her treatment for a while. Her cancer was aggressive. Scary situation. I am not comfortable with you working during chemo, especially around children during the cold and flu season."

"You mean I can't go in the center?" I asked. "Even if I stay in my office?"

"Could you really stay in your office?" Mendez asked.

"No," Mike answered for me. I turned my head to look at him, annoyed by his quick reply.

"That is what I would do if it were my wife," Dr. Mendez said, speaking directly to Mike.

Speechless, I looked back and forth at the two of them. Conspiring against me. My shoulders dropped as I pulled my planner to my chest, pouting like a child. I felt like a little girl whose parents told her she couldn't go to the party. I just made peace that I had cancer, but now I had to give up my work too?

I was devastated but I understood it was for the best. This was serious. I never took a sick day. I worked through many a fever, sore throat, even pneumonia once, but cancer was different. I surrendered. Temporarily.

For the next few weeks, between scans and doctor appointments, I prepared for my forced medical leave. I planned to work from home, managing the schedule, payroll, ordering supplies, and whatever I could do from my phone and the computer. Allie and Darcie offered to handle the day-to-day operations before I even asked.

I thanked Allie again and hung up the phone. Over the years, she became a better director than me. She knew the licensing regulations inside and out. She was great with the staff and the kids. Parents loved her. I trusted her to make decisions when I wasn't there.

It was unsettling to be away from work, but I was more concerned about finances. As a business owner, I wore many hats. I had to pay extra people to do the work I did myself. It would be tight and I couldn't draw a paycheck while I was gone. I feared the strain on the bottom line, especially so soon after opening the second center. I worried about medical bills and wondered how all this would also affect our family finances. At night I stared at the ceiling worrying about that on top of everything else.

I pulled some files I would need for home and packed them in a box when Tony stopped by. He checked in from time to time to say 'hello' and to see if I had any new hires. He was a good salesman, after all.

"Moving out?" Tony joked, looking at the boxes on the floor.

Ugh. It was so hard to tell people I had cancer. I wasn't sure if saying those words out loud would ever get easier. I knew no other way than to blurt it out. Rip off the bandaid.

"Tony, I was diagnosed with breast cancer a few weeks ago. I will start chemo soon. I won't be able to come to the office for a while. I'll be working from home. I will be back though, after I beat this thing." I repeated the sentences, robotically and without eye contact, the same way I said it to so many parents and colleagues over the last couple weeks. When I found the nerve to look at Tony, tears filled his eyes.

"No, Jennifer. I can't believe it. You are too young," he said, shaking his head. "I will draw up the papers for you as soon as I get to the office."

"What papers?"

"For your insurance policy. Your policy pays out about $30,000 if you have a heart attack or are diagnosed with cancer. That's what that policy is for. I hope that helps. I am so sorry you are going through this."

I was speechless.

Tony explained again as my brain made sense of his words. I only bought the policies because Tony reminded me of my dad. I would not have known about that policy if Tony hadn't stopped on that day. Tony emailed the papers that evening and my doctor completed the forms. We had a check deposited into our savings account a week later.

I believed God sent Tony to my office back then. Not just any insurance salesman, but Tony, a man who reminded me of the father I missed so much. If it had been anyone else, I would have taken his business card and never called him. Instead, I invited him into my office and bought life insurance policies on the spot. God knew what I needed back then. God was in the details. God's hands were in this. All over this. I said a prayer of gratitude and went to sleep. Blissful, wonderful sleep. That was the first full night of sleep I had in weeks.

* *

"I have an idea," Mike announced as he walked out of his office into the family room on Friday afternoon. The kids looked up from their building blocks and I put down my book.

"We are going to dinner and then shopping at Ikea," Mike said. "We are going to get something for Mommy."

"Yay!" the kids yelled, putting their blocks in the bin. "What are we getting for Mommy?"

"What do we need at Ikea?" I asked. I really didn't want to go anywhere. It was cold outside and my pajamas were calling my name.

"It's a surprise," he said, clapping his hands to hurry us along. "Get your shoes and coats on. Let's go."

Mike pulled into the parking lot of Bahama Breeze. I loved it there because it reminded me of a tropical vacation. Mike knew that. We went to a resort in Jamaica on our honeymoon and the island atmosphere brought back sweet memories. *I could really use a vacation right now*, I thought. This was as close as I would get for a while.

We had a fun dinner with the kids. They loved their fruity drinks and we ordered two desserts to share. Their eyes got so big and their mouths opened wide as the waitress set down the oversized plates of chocolate goodness. I soaked it all in, ignoring the chocolate dripping down Kade's chin. Mike and Kalea fought over the last bite of brownie with their spoons, making her giggle. I was so glad Mike convinced us to come out tonight. This was just what I needed. After I cleaned up the sticky fingers and chins, we piled in the car and drove to Ikea.

"Why are we going to Ikea?" I asked, hoping Mike would answer this time.

"You'll see. I have an idea," he said as he hopped out of the car.

"Let's go kids," he said, "Let's go shopping for Mommy!"

As we walked through the sliding doors, the kids skipped ahead. I had no idea what Mike was thinking. We didn't need furniture and this was not the time to make a big purchase. We weaved through the store, the kids stopping to sit on miscellaneous chairs and sofas and beds. Finally, Mike ran ahead of us, turned around, arms stretched wide.

"Okay, look around and find one you like."

We were surrounded by office furniture. I was still confused.

"I'm going to arrange our bedroom to fit a desk in there," Mike explained. "I will set up your computer and your printer so you can work upstairs from the bedroom. I'm going to make it really nice and comfortable for you."

I knew he was trying to help. It was such a sweet gesture. As hard as I tried, I couldn't stop the tears from falling, right there in the middle of Ikea.

"What's wrong? Mike asked as he grabbed me by the shoulders, the color draining from his face. The kids spun around on the office chairs.

"I'm sorry," I sobbed. "Thank you. This is so incredibly sweet."

"Then why are you crying?"

"I just don't want this. I don't want to work from home! I don't want to have chemo! I don't want to have cancer."

Mike pulled me to him and hugged me.

"Hey, I know. I hate this too. Let me do this for you," he said, lifting my chin to look him in the eyes. "We are going to make this work."

"Okay," I nodded, wiping my tears. "But as soon as this is over, that desk is out of there."

"Deal," Mike said, smiling. "Now pick one."

We both laughed. The kids came over and hugged my legs.

"Pick one, mommy!" Kade said.

* *

I had several tests scheduled that day. To reduce the days missed at work and the number of explanations I had to give to Mom for my absence, I convinced the nurse to schedule most of them in one day. Mike had to go out of town unexpectedly and asked me to reschedule, but I refused. I had an MRI and a heart test in the morning and a PET-scan in the afternoon. It was going to be a long day.

I shivered in the thin hospital gown on the hard table as the nurse straightened my IV line and left the room. The MRI was loud, those noises making me uncomfortable. I cried alone in the room begging for it to be over soon. This was all new to me. Outside of giving birth,

I was never in the hospital before.

"We will be in to get you soon," the nurse said over the intercom. I tried to relax on the table. It was more than a few minutes before the nurse entered the room.

"There are men working on the roof. There is a glass ceiling above us. We called to ask the men to move away from the roof so we can get you out of the machine, but the foreman refused to stop the job," she said. I heard the frustration in her voice. I was wearing a hospital gown but it was open with no way to get up without exposing myself.

"We have a plan. I grabbed some nurses from the next office. We are going to hold a sheet over your head so you can cover up and we will walk you out the door. Is that okay?"

"Sure," I said. I didn't have much choice. Five nurses held the sheet while I stood up and walked into the hallway. The exodus didn't help my frazzled nerves. I was taken to another room to wait for my heart test. Recliners lined the back wall, each one separated by a thin curtain. A while later, a nurse sat down in the chair next to me.

"We are having a problem with your insurance. They will not authorize the tests you scheduled for today. I am scheduling a bone scan and CT. By the time you get the sonogram of your heart done, I should know more. Would you like me to fit you in this afternoon or would you rather come in another day?"

"I wanted to get everything done today," I said, my voice shaky with emotion.

"You sure you don't want to go home after the heart test? It's been a lot today."

"No, I really don't want to come back here again."

"Okay," she said, handing me a tissue. "I will work my magic for you. The nurse will be down in a bit to take you upstairs for the sonogram."

I felt so alone and confused. I didn't know how to navigate all of this.

"Hello, dear," said a petite older woman with short gray hair and kind blue eyes peeking through the curtains. "May I come in?"

I nodded. She pushed back the curtain and sat in the chair next to me.

"These ugly curtains aren't soundproof. I thought you could use some company," she said, and within minutes, we were laughing. When her husband returned from his test, she introduced us. The three of us chatted until the nurse came to get me. I hugged them, thanked them, and said goodbye.

"You take care, my dear," she said. I waved to her as I followed the nurse out of the room. I was feeling better and ready to deal with the rest of the day.

Thank you, God. I know that was you.

After the heart test, the nurse escorted me to the room for the scan. A large man wearing glasses and sitting at the computer introduced himself as John. I climbed on another cold, flat table. I didn't bother to stop the tears quietly falling down my face. It had been such a long day.

John had his back to me at the computer but asked me the usual questions. The bone scan took about 30 minutes. We talked about my diagnosis and all the tests I had that day. He told me about his mom's battle with cancer.

"Cancer isn't fair. What is happening to you is awful. I am sorry you have to go through this," he said. His words were sincere. He talked to me like a person and not a patient. He acknowledged that this situation sucked. I didn't realize how much I needed to hear that.

"You are going to have hard days. Really hard days," he continued. "But you are going to be okay, just like my mom."

When the test was over, he walked me to yet another waiting room while the doctor reviewed the scans to make sure no additional pictures were needed. I picked up another magazine, flipped through a few pages, and put it down. All I wanted was to go home.

"Okay, Jennifer," John's big voice called from the hallway just outside the door. "You are free to go, but you are going to wait until the doctor calls you next week to tell you that everything looks okay."

It took me a second to realize what he just said to me.

"Thank you," I said. "For everything."

"You take care. You can do this."

* *

Nancy called. My wig arrived. She wanted to show me how to wear it properly and to care for it. I wasn't excited to get it.

"It matches your color so well," Nancy said, holding the wig against my hair to compare. "See? Perfect." She pulled my hair back, placed the wig on my head, and snapped the clips in the front. I never knew wigs worked like that. I glanced in the mirror and used my foot to turn my chair toward Nancy.

"How do I take care of it? How do I wash it?" I asked.

"I'll get you what you need," she said and pulled a bottle of shampoo from the shelf. She told me how to brush and wash my wig and how important it was to dry it on the wig form. I half-listened as I scratched my head, inadvertently moving the wig off-center.

"Let me fix that," Nancy said, smiling. "You have to watch. Nothing gives away a wig more than when it sits off your natural hairline."

"That's okay," I said and abruptly pulled the wig off my head. Nancy gently took the wig and placed it carefully in the box.

"I need to get home anyway. I will figure it out," I said, reaching for my purse and the bag of supplies.

"Sure thing. Good luck with everything. You give me a call when you need me," she said, reminding me of her offer to shave my head when the time came.

"Thank you." I walked to the exit. I was not ready for this.

When I got home, I didn't stop to drop my purse on the counter before I went upstairs to stash the wig and bag of supplies. My phone rang on the way up the steps. It was Dr. Barton's office. I put the bags on the bathroom counter and sat on the bed.

"Hi, Jennifer. This is Caroline from Dr. Barton's office. I wanted to check in with you about how your port surgery went and make sure you were ready to go next week?"

"I didn't have port surgery," I said, confused.

"You don't have a port?" she asked. "You need that before you start chemo!" She sounded alarmed. "Hold, please." She left me to listen to an instrumental version of a Richard Marx song. My heart raced as I paced in my bedroom waiting on hold.

"Jennifer? You still there?" Caroline asked, interrupting my spiraling thoughts. I didn't want to delay my first chemo.

"Okay. We can get you scheduled for the first surgery slot that morning for your port then you can go straight to the chemo lab for treatment. Otherwise, you have the surgery and wait a week for the port to heal. It will make for a very long day though. Does that sound okay? If not, we can schedule the port surgery and push back your chemo."

"That's fine. I can do that," I said, relieved to stay on schedule.

I went downstairs to tell Mike. I added the potatoes to the roast and put it back in the oven for dinner. I sat on the couch to relax for a few minutes, but woke up an hour later as Mom pulled the roast out of the oven and plates out of the cabinet.

"I'm sorry, Mom," I said, jumping up. "I didn't mean to fall asleep."

"Come eat," she said, waving away my apology.

I finished cleaning up after dinner and told Kalea to get her pajamas and meet me upstairs. I promised her a bubble bath in the jacuzzi tub in my bathroom tonight.

I ran up the stairs, remembering to grab a towel from the linen closet. I walked into the bathroom and found Kalea at the counter, holding my wig.

"Is this for your Halloween costume, Mommy?" she asked with an excited smile on her face.

I forgot to put the wig away when the nurse called earlier. Kalea was distracted by the wig and didn't notice how long it took me to answer while I prayed for the right words.

"Remember when I told you that Mommy was sick?" I asked.

"Yes," she said, her smile fading.

"My doctor will give me medicine to make me better, but that medicine will make me lose my hair. Just for a little while. Remember when we talked about that?" I asked her.

She nodded her head.

"Well, when I lose my hair, I get to wear this fun wig," I continued, smiling big so I didn't cry. How did I make her feel good about this when I didn't?

"Mommy is a little embarrassed about not having any hair," I whispered, my voice cracking. "I don't want people to see me with a shiny bald head."

"You would look silly with no hair, Mommy," Kalea giggled. "I wouldn't want to be bald either," she said, shaking her head, her eyes wide.

"Right?" I smiled. "So do you think I will look okay in this wig? Do you want me to try it on?"

"Yes! I want to see it!" she squealed, clapping and jumping up and down.

I brushed my hair back, placed the wig on my head, and pushed the clips like Nancy showed me. It wasn't as hard as I thought. Kalea reached up and touched the hair.

"You look like a princess, Mommy. You look pretty," Kalea said, her smile growing even bigger. "I like it, Mommy."

"Do you want to try it on?" I asked her. Her mouth opened wide in delight. "Can I Mommy? Can I?"

I put the wig on Kalea's head and her face beamed, a little girl playing dress up. She admired herself in the mirror, running her fingers through the long wig and turning her head from side to side.

"Can I wear this sometimes, Mommy?" she asked.

"Maybe," I said, praying she would never have to go through this.

I sat on my knees on the floor next to her and spoke to her in the mirror.

"Mommy is a little sad and scared. I don't want anyone to know about my wig yet," I told her. "Can it be our little secret for a while?" Kalea was a 6-year old chatterbox.

"Yes, Mommy. I won't tell anyone," and she made the motion of zipping her lips as I took the wig off of her head and carefully placed it back in the box, like Nancy did earlier.

I ran the bath, adding extra bubbles. Kalea played in the tub and squealed at the mountain of foam that formed when I turned on the jets. She didn't bring up the wig again. I was relieved she seemed fine with the wig.

I still wasn't.

* *

Tomorrow was the big day. We had to be at the hospital at 5 in the morning to register for surgery. I had an appointment with Dr. Mendez at 9:30 followed by an informational session with the nurse, and chemo at 11. The nurse said chemo would be about 4 hours on the first

THE IN-BETWEEN IS EVERYTHING

day. I wouldn't be home when the kids got home from school like I hoped.

I made a list of the things Christi told me to pack for chemo: a blanket, a water bottle, a book, hard candies, and a pad to take notes. Making lists and checking them off made me feel prepared and in control.

I had never felt so out of control in my life.

I dug in the back of the closet. What did a chemo bag look like anyway? Finally, I found a brand new one I bought at a party a while back. I removed the plastic wrapping and added a book from the pile I never had time to read. I packed a notebook and a bag of mints. I left a water bottle on the kitchen counter to fill in the morning and picked up the beautiful crocheted blanket my mom made me and put it in the bag.

I remembered the night I told Mom I was sick. I didn't want to break her heart. My legs were weak as I walked up the stairs to her bedroom and knocked on her door. She was watching television in her chair. I sat on her bed like I did a thousand times before. She was smiling and I didn't want to be the reason her smile went away.

"I have to tell you something, Mom," I blurted out, using my professional voice so I didn't cry. "I have breast cancer...but I am going to be okay."

"What?" Mom said, placing her hands on the arms of the chair, a mixture of shock and fear replacing her smile.

"When did this happen?" Mom asked. She sat up in her recliner, learning forward, a look of disbelief on her face. I completely blindsided her but there was no other way to do it. Is there a way to gently break the news your daughter has cancer?

"I found out a while ago, but I didn't want to tell you until I had a plan."

"What is the plan?"

I explained it as simply as I could.

"I start chemo in a couple of weeks. Then I will have a double mastectomy. I have an amazing doctor. I will get through all of this in the next 6 to 9 months and then I will be okay."

Mom didn't say anything. She was processing the terrible news.

"I am sorry I didn't tell you sooner. I waited until the doctors had a plan."

"Do the kids know?"

"No, not yet. We are going to tell them soon. I am not looking forward to that. We will tell them only what they need to know. I don't want to scare them."

"Those kids are smart," she said. "They will have lots of questions."

"I know. We will answer them the best we can."

Mom sat in silence, staring straight ahead.

"This is going to suck, but I can do this."

Mom nodded her head.

I told Mom everything would be normal again, and I almost convinced myself too. I walked out of her room, relieved, but telling Mom stripped away the last bit of denial I had been clinging to the last few weeks.

My secret was out.

Chapter Seven

"Storms make trees take deeper roots."
DOLLY PARTON

After I told Mom, she did what she had done my whole life, showing me how much she loved me in a million little ways. She offered to drive Kade to half-day kindergarten, cook and clean, and help wherever she was needed. I told her Dr. Mendez said I had to work from home. I mentioned that my laptop might be too old to run the accounting software I needed. A week later, a brand new laptop arrived. Christi suggested a special mouthwash to help with the mouth sores caused by chemo. The next day, that mouthwash was sitting on my counter. I was overwhelmed but not surprised by Mom's thoughtfulness and generosity. She was the sweetest soul I knew.

One night after putting the kids to bed, I stopped by her room to say goodnight.

"I have something for you," Mom said, jumping from her chair. She placed a bag on the bed and pulled out a beautiful pink crocheted blanket with a small cancer ribbon crocheted on the corner.

"I thought you could take it with you to your treatments."

"I love it, Mom," I said, admiring the handmade blanket. "Thank you."

I could think of nothing better than to wrap up in Mom's love while I experienced something so terrifying. Mom always knew what I needed. I saved the blanket for my first chemo treatment. I was excited to put it in my chemo bag.

I finished packing and set out my clothes for the next day: yoga pants, a zipper hoodie and a tank top, so the nurses could easily access the port on my upper arm. Before I went to bed, I checked in on the kids.

I watched each of them sleep for a while. I stroked their hair and studied their little faces. My nerves and emotions bubbled to the top, but I had to do this for them.

God, give me strength. Thank you for making me a mom. Thank you for trusting these children to me and Mike. I want to watch them grow up. I want to be there for the teen years. Cheer for them at their games. Watch them throw their caps in the air at graduation. Even cry when I send them off to college. I will do anything. Give me the strength to do this. I can't do this on my own.

I pulled myself together and went downstairs to clean up before bed. I found a few matchbox cars on the coffee table and held them to my chest. Kade loved his cars. He took one with him everywhere. I put two of them away, the last one in my chemo bag. I took one of Kalea's crayon drawings from the fridge and put it in my bag too. Kalea was always drawing pictures. Jewelry wasn't allowed in the hospital, but I tucked the necklace Mike gave me on our first Christmas, the one I wore every day, into a pocket inside the bag. I clipped a picture of the kids inside the notebook along with the bookmark, with a poem called "Don't Quit" that my dad kept near his computer. Including my mom's blanket, I had something from each of my family members with me.

I set my clock for 3:30 in the morning. I couldn't sleep. I turned off the alarm clock at 3:27. Adrenaline helped me out of bed. I got a shower and woke Mike. I placed the kids lunchboxes on the counter and their backpacks on the floor. Mom was getting the kids off to school that morning. Last night, I left them a note on the counter. I gathered my things and set them next to the laundry room door.

Mike came downstairs and grabbed his laptop and work bag from his office. Without a word, he threw my bag over his shoulder and loaded the car.

"Ready?" he broke the thick silence when he returned.

I wasn't ready, but walked out the door behind him.

We didn't talk on the way to the hospital. Neither of us knew what to say. Phillip Phillips' song, "Home" came on the radio. The lyrics described the moment perfectly. I was holding onto Mike down this unfamiliar road. I reached over to hold his hand. The song was still playing when we pulled into the parking garage. I looked over at Mike.

I was not alone.

* *

We walked through the long hallways and took the elevator to outpatient registration. Mike took a seat in the waiting room while I checked in with the receptionist.

"I'll bring you back in a few minutes," the nurse told Mike as she closed the door behind us and ushered me down the hall. She handed me a gown and those goofy hospital socks that came up to my knees. I changed into the gown, pulling the strings tight in the back, and pulled the socks up high for warmth. A few minutes later, the nurse returned with a handful of vials for blood work. As she rubbed my arm to find a good vein, she introduced herself as Marilyn. She was probably in her early 60's. She was tall with thin grey hair and her piercing blue eyes looked at me from behind wire-rimmed glasses. She had a gentle nature and something about her said she was wise.

"How are you doing?" she asked. I could tell she knew my story.

"I'm okay," I said automatically, realizing how silly that sounded as it came out of my mouth. "I have to get a port placed today and start chemo this morning. I have breast cancer."

"I read your chart. I am so sorry," Marilyn said, shaken. "You are too young." She chose a good spot to dive into my arm and I shivered as she cleaned the area with alcohol. Marilyn guided the needle into the vein and I watched my blood fill one vial after another, amazed there was any left after the last few weeks. We talked about our families and our faith.

"Do you mind if I pray for you?" she asked as she finished charting information.

"I would love that," I answered, thankful for not only a kind nurse, but a Christian one. She prayed for my port surgery, my chemo, and my general health.

"Amen," we both said. I thanked her and gave her a hug.

"God bless you. I will keep you in my prayers," she told me before she left to get Mike. I saw her wipe tears from her eyes as she turned around.

Mike came in and sat on the bed with me. Within a minute or two, a male attendant came to escort me to pre-op. He was tall and young and full of energy, even so early in the morning.

"Hey there! I am Steve. I am your taxi driver this morning."

"Love you," Mike said and he kissed me goodbye. Marilyn said she would escort him back to the waiting room but he didn't move. He stood there watching as Steve pushed me down the hall. I turned my head to look back at him as long as I could. My Superman, he couldn't save me this time.

Chapter Eight

"Breathe, darling. This is just a chapter.
It's not your whole story."

S.C. LOURIE

Here goes nothing, I thought as Steve maneuvered the bed down one long corridor after another. I felt self-conscious as we passed hospital staff, patients, and visitors. Steve distracted me by making noises and sound effects with every stop and turn.

"The doctors are going to take real good care of you," he said. "You will be out of here before you know it." He seemed so silly, but he knew exactly what he was doing. His kind eyes told me his antics were intentional, his goal to make his patients feel better.

When we got to our destination, the pre-op room was crowded. An old man grimaced and rubbed his abdomen. A child cried as a nurse comforted him. A woman snored loudly. Steve parked my bed like an SUV in a shopping mall parking lot on Black Friday, complete with more sound effects. It was a tight fit, but he did so with ease.

"You're good," I said.

"I've done this a time or two," he said. "Would you like a warm blanket?"

"Would I ever!" I said. It was so cold in the hospital.

He laughed and opened a door and pulled a hot blanket out like Mom pulled a casserole out of the oven. He covered me with the blanket. After spending an hour in a backless gown and knee high socks, it was like hot chocolate after playing in the snow.

"Good luck to you. I am leaving you in good hands. God bless you," Steve said as he waved and turned, rushing off to pick up another patient.

Look at God! He sent me Sweet Marilyn and Speedy Steve that morning. He knew what I needed. I watched the staff buzz around the room. Organized chaos. I was coming to temperature under my blanket when a man in a white coat appeared at my bedside and pulled my file out of some invisible place under my bed. He had short blond hair and a kind face and introduced himself as my anesthesiologist. "You have a long day ahead of you, my dear," he commented, shaking his head as he read my file.

"I have to go from here to chemo today," I said. I figured he already knew from my chart but I babbled when I was nervous.

"I see that. We will get you out of here. I promise," he assured me, resting his hand on my shoulder. "God bless you," He squeezed a syringe into my IV. "I'll see you in there."

I woke up to a nurse filling out paperwork on the counter next to the window in another room. The morning sun was bright in the morning sky.

"Good morning, sleepyhead," said the nurse. "How are you feeling?"

"I'm okay, I guess," I said, noticing a dull ache in my right arm. Bandages and what looked like an IV tube were secured and taped to it. A few seconds later, Mike appeared from behind the curtain. More magic.

He looked tired and worried, but relieved. He sat with me while I drank orange juice and ate a few crackers. The nurse gave me discharge instructions and a bag to hold in case I needed to vomit. The anesthesia made me nauseous, but the nurse said it would pass. I took longer to wake up after surgery than they expected. The nurse called the cancer center to tell them we would be late.

We made the short drive from the hospital to the cancer center. Mike helped me out of the car and up to the 5th floor. The nausea passed, but I felt loopy and weak. Before we took a seat in the waiting room, I accepted one of those free knit caps from the basket on the counter. I picked one with different shades of purple and shoved it in the bottom of my chemo bag.

We didn't wait long before the nurse called us back to see Dr. Mendez. He wanted to meet briefly to answer any last-minute questions. Only one was on my mind.

"How long until I lose my hair?" I asked.

Dr. Mendez paused, knowing he was about to tell me something I didn't want to hear.

"Your hair will be gone the next time I see you. I'd say 10 to 14 days."

It was October 3rd. My brother's wedding was on October 13th. I scheduled a family photo shoot for October 14th. Ugh. I prayed my hair would stick around long enough for the wedding and our family photos. I wanted pictures of us before cancer changed everything.

The nurse knocked on the door. They were ready for me. Along the hallway were open rooms of beige recliners separated by beige curtains. Who decorated these places? Men and women sat shackled to poles and IV bags. A sort of medical prison. My heart beat fast. This was happening. We turned a corner to more beige recliners and curtains. Some patients slept, some stared at the small televisions attached to their recliners, and some visited with friends and family. An older gentleman sat up on the side of his recliner playing cards with a friend, laughing and carrying on about someone cheating.

My nurse, Shari, motioned for me to sit in a recliner in the corner. Mike took a seat in a nearby chair. Shari pulled a stool between us and opened a file of papers on her lap. She pulled out information on the drugs, the precautions, and the harsh side effects I could expect. Shari was as uplifting as one could be as she discussed the risks of infection and sudden death. Finally, she told me about an injection I would have on Friday, two days after chemo. The injection helped my body make white blood cells to boost my immune system. She left us alone for a moment, leaving the curtain open behind her.

The recliners were arranged in a circle. An elderly woman and her husband sat directly across from me, both sleeping. Next to them sat a large man fully reclined and snoring so loudly, the IV line vibrated all the way to the top of the pole, causing his IV bag to sway back and forth in rhythm. On the other side of him was a woman who looked like she drew her eyebrows on with a broad tip marker. She was eating Pringles like she was in a movie theater and my recliner was the big screen. Shari returned and hung a clear bag of liquid on my pole, carefully connecting the tubes.

"This is just one of your pre-meds. You will have some fluids, nausea medication, and Benadryl. I'll be back to check on you in a few minutes. Can I get you anything?"

"I think I am good," I answered her, noticing the woman with the brows exchanged her Pringles for a bag of popcorn. "Do you mind pulling the curtain?"

"I'm sorry, no can do. This is your first chemo. I have to watch you to make sure everything is okay. No allergic reactions or other emergencies."

Seriously? If I wasn't concerned about being a double feature for all of my new chemo buddies, I might have asked what she meant by 'other emergencies'. Instead I wrapped up in my mom's blanket and turned to my side, the best I could shackled to a metal pole. It wasn't long before the first bag was empty and Shari returned to start the second bag of fluids.

"This will help you with nausea after your treatment. You have a prescription for nausea meds, but you might not need them. You let us know how you do. We will help you manage it," she said. When she left, the curtain got caught on the small file cabinet and created the perfect barrier between me and the woman with the brows. I breathed a sigh of relief.

It was short lived, though. A moment later, she shifted in her seat, stretching her neck to regain her view. Her face appeared over the file cabinet like a cat slinking toward its prey. Mike and I exchanged glances.

Shari said I could have lunch during my treatment. I hadn't eaten anything, but crackers and orange juice in recovery. Mike ran to a nearby restaurant to get some food, but promised to hurry. He didn't want to leave me alone.

I reclined back in my seat and held a pillow strategically across my chest. It was to no avail. The woman's face again appeared, this time slowly over my pillow like a hippopotamus emerging from the swamp. Relentless.

When Mike returned, we ate lunch and tried to pretend the other patients weren't there. Mike worked on his laptop and I read my book, which also served as a shield. A while later, Mike tapped me on the leg. With a Pringles can open in her lap and her wig tilted far to the left, the woman with the brows was sound asleep.

Hallelujah!

Shari returned as we were rejoicing. We felt like the teacher walked in on us misbehaving.

"This is Benadryl to prevent an allergic reaction. It makes you very sleepy. Would you like to use the bathroom before you get too much in you? All these fluids make you have to pee."

"I better go. Do you have to unplug me?" I asked.

"Oh no, I can't do that. Wheel the pole with you. The bathroom is right around the corner." Mike helped me stand and Shari walked me around the corner and pointed to the bathroom. I felt a little woozy so I leaned back on the wall. The bathroom was occupied.

"Is this your first time?" an older man wearing overalls and a flannel shirt asked. He was very nervous and jittery.

"Yes," I answered. "First time."

"I heard the nurse tell you about that shot. My wife can tell you. It's bad."

I hadn't seen this man before. How did he hear my conversation with the nurse? The door to the bathroom opened and a woman in a wheelchair came out. Her husband jumped behind her and wheeled her to me.

"This girl is going to get the shot on Friday," he told his wife. She looked up with wide eyes and clapped her hands silently in a nervous fit.

"The shot!" she said in an eerie whisper, her eyes almost looking through me. "Don't take the shot!"

Her hands kept 'clapping' as the man wheeled her away. The interaction was like a scene in a horror movie. The wife turned back to look at me as her husband pushed her around the corner. I grabbed my IV pole and took refuge in the bathroom. It was awkward using the bathroom attached to my skinny sidekick, but I managed. I was more worried I'd find Haley Joel Osment in the hallway when I was done.

I wheeled the pole back to my chair and Mike helped me into it. Benadryl coursing through my veins really wiped me out. A while later, Shari woke me when the Benadryl drip was complete. She would be

69

back with my first bag of chemo.

I didn't recognize Shari when she returned. She was covered from head to toe in what looked like a yellow hazmat suit, a plastic mask covering her entire face. In her hands was a bag with a skull and cross-bones printed on its side. I was too dopey to read all the words, but I saw the word "CAUTION" at least three times.

What in the world? Shari was dressed like those government workers in E.T. just to handle the bag, and this stuff would soon flow through my veins?

Even the heavy dose of Benadryl wasn't enough to keep me from praying on that one. I closed my eyes and prayed hard for God to direct this poison straight to the tumor and protect the rest of my body from the collateral damage. I prayed myself to sleep. Or maybe it was the Benadryl.

After the first bag, Shari returned to administer the second while I slept. I dreamed I was swimming in the pool and took in a nose full of chlorinated water. I was stirred awake by a burning sensation in my nose. My eyes shot open and I waved at Mike, too sleepy to speak. I was scared. Was this an allergic reaction? Was this one of those 'emergencies'?

"My nose is burning," I said to Mike when I found the words. He jumped up and called for Shari, his work papers fell to the floor.

"What's wrong?" I heard her say, running toward my chair.

"She said her nose is burning," Mike said in a panic.

"Oh, that is the cytoxan. You were sleeping so I couldn't warn you. Some patients experience that burning nose toward the end of the bag. It will go away once the bag is done. You are almost finished."

Just a tiny bit of liquid remained in the bag. It was a good thing because my eyes watered like a dripping faucet. My nose felt like someone set a fire inside my nostrils.

Finally, Shari, dressed in her yellow E.T. suit, removed the bag and disposed of it in a special wastebasket. She returned in plain scrubs and separated me from the thin pole that carried my medicine.

"All set," Shari said, bandaging my arm. "Everything went well. You take care of yourself. A nurse is on call 24 hours. Call if you need anything. Someone will call to check in on you tomorrow."

Mike folded my blanket and packed my bag while Shari helped me out of the recliner. I felt woozy and waterlogged. Mike helped me walk out of the cancer center and into the car. He shut the door and I sunk into the seat.

Aside from being tired, I felt okay. So far, so good. One chemo treatment down, five more to go. I can do this. Mike started the car and grabbed my hand. I squeezed back as hard as I could.

"Let's go home," he said.

As we exited the parking lot, Mike turned on the radio. That Phillip Phillips' song was playing again.

"Yes. I want to go home."

Chapter Nine

Sitting with a group of people as they discussed their bad days.
Person #1: I skipped my morning coffee and have had this
nagging headache all day.
Person #2: I'm getting a cold. I am going home to curl up on
the couch.
Person #3: I am so tired. I stayed up too late watching
television last night.
Person #1: How are you, Jen?
(Super exhausted, stomach a wreck, bones aching)
Me: I'm good.

We pulled into the driveway and the thought of seeing the kids carried my weak legs to the door. The kitchen lights made me squint but I saw Mom at the sink. I smelled something delicious cooking on the stove and heard the theme song from a children's program on the television. After a ridiculously long day in a clinical environment, I breathed in the familiar sights and sounds of home.

"Mommy!" The kids jumped from the couch. They hugged me. Hard. I leaned on the counter, my arm throbbing with the unexpected movement.

"Easy guys, Mommy is tired. She had a long day," Mike said.

"I am so happy to see you guys," I said. I sat on the stool and pulled them close. Kalea put her head in my lap and Kade wrapped his arms around my legs. They sensed that I was not feeling well.

73

JENNIFER LILLEY COLLINS

"I made chicken soup," Mom said. "The kids already ate."

Kalea and Kade went back to the family room to play. Mom served me soup like she did when I was little. I wondered if making me chicken soup made her feel better, like making chocolate cookies for my kids did for me. It was so good. After being cold all day, the flavorful broth warmed me from the inside out. I was hungry but afraid to eat too much with all that toxic skull-and-crossbones stuff coursing through my veins. When I stood and picked up my bowl, my hands shook.

"Just sit." She took the bowl and cleaned up the kitchen as I told her about the nurse who prayed for me, the kind anesthesiologist, and the other patients..

Mike gave the kids their baths. When they were little, he filled the tub with so much bubble bath, only two tiny faces poked out from the bubbles overflowing the tub. He dumped in every plastic boat and squirt toy and let them stay until their teeth chattered and their lips turned blue. Oh my. I used to get so annoyed when I came home from work to a wet floor, lingering bubbles on the back wall, and a path of towels and clothes from bathroom to bedroom.

"The bathroom never looks like that when I bathe the kids," I snapped one night.

"Just because I don't do it your way, doesn't mean my way is wrong. And..." he added. "We always have more fun!".

He was right. He was more fun. He didn't have to clean up the mess, though. How serious I was back then. Get in and get out. Not too many bubbles. Not too many toys. Mike made bathtime an event. I was starting to see things his way these days.

I insisted on putting them to bed. I didn't want to miss those precious minutes at bedtime even if climbing the stairs felt like scaling Mount Everest.

"What happened to your arm, Mommy?" Kade asked.

"The doctor put a button in my arm that helps the nurses give me my medicine," I said, trying to answer so he would understand. I sat down on his bed.

"Oh...do you mean like a button on a shirt or a button on a tv?"

"The button helps push the medicine in faster to get rid of the cancer."

74

"Like a superpower button?".

"Something like that," I said, smiling and running my fingers through his hair. I kissed him again on his forehead and lightly tapped his nose with my finger.

"Night, Buddy. I love you."

"Goodnight," he said with a yawn. "Love you, Mommy."

I stood in his doorway for a few minutes and gazed at him. Snuggled in bed, smelling of wild cherry shampoo and bubble gum toothpaste. Footy pajamas and goodnight kisses. Now this was what it was all about.

I slowly made it down the steps and collapsed on the couch. I turned on the television and woke up around two in the morning. Mike was sleeping on the loveseat, his feet dangling over the edge. Today was hard on him too. He didn't want to wake me up, but didn't want to leave me alone. I covered Mike with a blanket and walked to the kitchen for a glass of water. I tried to be quiet, but Mike woke up. He walked me upstairs and I fell asleep instantly.

When I woke in the morning, I felt like I hadn't slept in days. I struggled to get Kalea ready for school. I drank hot tea and ate a piece of toast. I wondered when all those side effects would hit me.

Kade was in the afternoon kindergarten class. I was disappointed when he wasn't scheduled for the morning session. Leaving work at lunchtime to drop him off would be challenging. The morning was a better fit. I preferred to get up and get things done. Kade was an early riser too. While I complained, God knew that was the best option. It wasn't about my work schedule. God knew what He was doing. I was able to get Kalea off to school and spend time with Kade before the afternoon session. His plan was always better than mine.

We snuggled on the couch and watched *Peter Rabbit.* Kade played with his blocks and cars while I rested on the couch. I helped Kade get dressed and brush his teeth and Mom took him to school. I called the center soon after they left so I could take a nap while both kids were gone.

"I didn't expect to hear from you today," Darcie said. "How are you feeling?"

"I'm tired. Really tired, but hanging in there. All okay?"

"All good," said Darcie and she filled me in on attendance and the schedule. "Go get some rest. I will talk to you tomorrow."

I woke up when the kids came home. No matter how much sleep I got, the exhaustion never went away. Forcing myself out of bed, I walked to the bathroom and brushed my hair, wondering how much longer my hair would last. Walking downstairs, I smelled something wonderful coming from the kitchen. Mom already had dinner in the oven. She really was the best.

I checked the kid's homework folders and emptied their backpacks. My eyes watered and my throat was sore. I hoped I wasn't getting a cold. I felt more awake by dinnertime and looked forward to a family meal. Mom's roast smelled delicious. I filled my plate with roast and potatoes. Everything looked so good. I took one bite and swallowed.

The pain was indescribable. Sandpaper on my throat. I felt that small bite travel down my esophagus. Every excruciating inch. I drank a full glass of water. I held back tears. I was hungry and wanted to eat, but I couldn't.

Later, my food scraped and clawed its way through my entire digestive system. I could only tolerate heavily iced water. I was hungry and miserable. Mom suggested frozen fruit bars and Mike went to the store to get some. Cold was the only thing that soothed my wounded insides. I lived on frozen fruit bars for days.

On Friday, I had to get "the shot". Pam called me back right away. I was surprised how emotional I was just being there. As Pam prepared the supplies for my injection, I told her about the lady in the wheelchair.

"Don't worry about her. Everyone is different. Think of this shot as a million construction workers inside your bones producing more white blood cells. It can make your bones ache, but you need it. Call us if you have any problems," she said, then plunged the needle into my arm without warning.

Maybe she was right. Maybe that lady had a bad reaction. I left the cancer center and called Darcie from the parking lot. I had supplies to drop off on my way home. Before I could enter the code, Darcie met me at the door, looking frazzled.

"Tyler had a blowout and Lily puked in the preschool bathroom at the same time," she said. "It has been a day! Tom has to work a double tonight. I've got to get the kids to dance class and basketball within a thirty minute window."

"Oh no! Did you get it cleaned up alright?" I asked, feeling instantly guilty. I knew how stressful it was when everything happened at once. "Do you need help tonight running the kids?"

"I got it covered. My dad can run somebody somewhere, but thanks." I heard someone yell from downstairs for Darcie.

"I have to go. You take care. I will talk to you later." Darcie shut the door.

* *

As I drove home, my eyes felt heavy and my heart was beating fast. I sat on the couch to catch my breath. I didn't notice Mom come downstairs.

"You should just take a nap."

"I might," I said. "I have Kari's party tonight." Mom looked confused and concerned.

"Mom, we will be sitting around eating snacks and placing orders. It is a home party, nothing crazy." She didn't look any less concerned.

"I won't stay long. I will visit a little bit, place my order, and come home."

I curled up on the couch. I was frustrated it took so much of my energy to do the simplest of things. I slept later than I intended. I planned to shower and curl my hair, but settled for brushing my teeth. I didn't feel well, but I wanted to go to the party, hang out with a bunch of girlfriends, and shop for bags I didn't need.

"You sure you have to go?" Mom asked, trying one last time to convince me to stay home.

"I'll be fine, Mom. I won't be long," I said and shut the front door behind me.

I made it down the driveway and onto the sidewalk. Kari's house was two doors up but it could have been in Canada. I took a few steps at a time until I made it to Kari's driveway.

Kari answered the door. The house was full of people already.

"Hey! Glad you made it. How *are* you?" she asked. "You feeling okay?"

"I'm good," I said as more guests arrived. I moved into the kitchen, grateful for the escape.

"Hi, Jen! How are you?" another neighbor asked. I answered and excused myself. I didn't want to talk about me tonight.

Since frozen fruit bars weren't available, I didn't eat. I filled my glass with ice water, grabbed a catalog, and found a seat on a folding chair next to the couch in the family room.

I opened the catalog and the words and pictures swirled on the page. A woman I didn't recognize sat down beside me. I moved over to give her more room and felt like I was going to fall from my chair. If I could have stood up, I would have gone home. I silently prayed for God to give me strength and to not let me make a spectacle of myself in front of all these people. The presenter whistled and everyone took their seats.

She introduced new products and passed around items while I held onto my chair. The woman next to me started coughing. It sounded like her lung was going to land in her lap.

Stay away from sick people ... weakened immune system ... low white cell counts.

I was scared and desperate. I had to get out of there. Dr. Mendez told me about the woman who almost died because she caught a cold. Here I was sitting next to Coughy McCougherson. I tried not to breathe. Why didn't I listen to Mom? When the presentation was over, I stood up as the room spun circles and carefully walked toward Kari.

"I am not feeling well. I will place an order online tomorrow. I'm sorry," I said and turned to leave.

"Wait. Let me walk you out. Are you sure you are okay? Can I walk you home?" she offered.

"No," I lied. "I will be fine. I'm just tired. Get back to your party."

She wanted to say more but I headed for the door. The cool air felt good on my hot skin. My house looked so far away and I instantly regretted not accepting Kari's offer to walk me home. I wondered if a passerby would notice me if I fell on the sidewalk. *Get a grip, Jen.* My legs were heavy and my feet hurt when they touched the ground. I wanted to sit down but knew I would never get back up again. *One step at a time. You're almost there.*

I had never been so happy to reach my front door. It took what energy I had left to change into my pajamas. I curled up on the couch and turned on the television. I woke up again in the middle of the night. Mike was on the loveseat, his legs dangling over the edge again. I never heard him come home from his out of town meeting. He left very early that morning, squeezed two days of work into one, and drove four hours to get back home. I didn't want to wake him.

I walked down the hall. Holding on tightly to the rail, I took the steps one at a time to our bedroom. Drinking all that ice water made me have to pee constantly. I leaned on the sink as I washed my hands...

I woke up on the bathroom floor, my head between the sink cabinets. I stayed there for a while, dozing on and off, until I was more alert. I sat up slowly, crawled out of the bathroom, and onto the bed. I felt my head. No blood. I slid off the bed to the floor and scooted to the hallway. Like a toddler, I went down the steps on my backside, one at a time. Pain shot through my body with each step. I pulled myself up by the stair rail and walked to the family room. I tapped Mike on the shoulder and he startled awake.

"I passed out upstairs," I whispered.

Mike looked confused, his eyes adjusting to see me.

"But you are standing here now,' Mike whispered back in a sleepy stupor. I would have laughed at his reply if I hadn't been so scared. He shook himself awake and walked me upstairs.

"You should have woken me up," he said. I collapsed on the bed, so thankful to be still.

Mike went to the bathroom and I pulled the covers over me when a pain so deep and strong gripped my body and didn't let go. I writhed in pain, unable to breathe. The pain subsided for a moment and just as I caught my breath, another wave swept over me, this time worse than the last. It happened again and again. There was nothing I could do.

Mike came out of the bathroom and dove toward the bed.

"What's wrong? What can I do?" he asked, terrified.

"I don't know," I said. "It hurts."

"What hurts?"

"Everything."

Mike tried to hold me but I pushed him away. I didn't want anything to touch me.

"Should I take you to the hospital?"

The thought of getting out of bed was too much. That woman in the wheelchair, she warned me. The pain was deep inside my bones. Every single one of them. I imagined construction workers with pick axes beating my bones from the inside. Relentless, evil construction workers.

It hurt to move, but it hurt more to stay still. My body contorted uncontrollably, desperately seeking relief from the pain. Mike begged me to let him call an ambulance, or to take me to the emergency room.

"The worst place for me is a crowded emergency room with a bunch of sick people," I said. "It's the shot. I have to ride it out."

The pain went on for hours. I was desperate for relief and for sleep. I felt like I was dying. I prayed for God to take me soon. I gave up.

Take me to heaven, Lord. Take me now. Please, Lord. Take me...

I opened my eyes and the early morning light poured through the window. I was still here. The bone pain was gone but my body ached all over, my muscles angry from fighting the pain. It hurt to move. It hurt to breathe, but I could handle that pain.

The on-call nurse confirmed the pain was due to the shot, or a side effect from chemotherapy. After a horrific night, I spent the rest of the day trying to make myself comfortable. Shower. Pajamas. Blankets. Tea. I slept off the fatigue, fear, and shame. I couldn't shake the guilt. One bad night and I was ready to die? Maybe I wasn't as strong as I thought.

Chapter Ten

"You have cancer? That sucks. If I found out I had cancer,
I would kill myself..."

FRIEND OF A FRIEND

This look alright?" Mike asked, trying on another button-down shirt. Mike hated formal clothes. He was already miserable, but he couldn't wear a t-shirt and basketball shorts to Chris' wedding.

"Perfect," I said. "I'm going to get Kalea dressed and then we need to go."

I checked my reflection one more time and pushed a stray piece of hair back into place. I was 10 days out from chemo. My face was puffy from the steroids but I was feeling better. I still had hair. Today was the wedding and our family pictures were tomorrow.

I brushed Kalea's hair and she put on the flower girl dress. She looked so pretty. Kade was already downstairs with Mom. Mike came down a few minutes later tugging on his collar and fussing with his tie.

"I already can't wait to take this off," he said. "You guys ready?". We piled in the car and drove to Carnegie. It was a crisp October day and puffy-white-clouds hung in a blue sky overhead.

Chris and Marissa said, "I do" in a beautiful ceremony. Kalea danced the night away with the other kids. Kade ran around and kept busy checking out the cookie table. We caught up with friends and family. I couldn't help but think of Dad. He would have had such a great time. His picture was displayed near a lit candle in his memory, but his absence was deeply felt.

When we got home, I put the kids to bed and went upstairs to change. I stared at myself in the mirror. I hoped my face wouldn't be so puffy in the morning for our photo shoot. I had the best of intentions, but I never purchased new outfits for us. I would find something in our closets tomorrow morning. It wasn't about the clothes anyway.

I got up early the next morning and showered first. I washed my hair and reached for the conditioner. My palms were covered with hair. I rinsed it from my hands and added my conditioner. My hands were full of hair again. So much hair.

I turned off the shower and grabbed a towel. I was afraid to look in the mirror. I turned my head, twisting my neck to see every angle. No bald spots. I ran my hands through my hair and strands stuck between my fingers. Oh no, not today. Just one more day. I finger-brushed my hair and blow-dried it on low. I couldn't style it. I pulled a blue sweater out of the closet and walked downstairs like a model with a book on her head, as if my hair would fall off in one piece if I moved too much. Mike and the kids were eating breakfast.

"My hair is falling out," I whispered to Mike and walked away. I didn't want to cry. I plastered a smile on my face and got the kids ready and out the door. We drove in silence to meet the photographer.

It was a gorgeous fall morning. Blue skies, puffy-white-clouds. The sunlight trickled through the leaves turned gold and burnt orange. We strolled along the trail, the crisp leaves crunching beneath our feet. The photographer chose the most amazing natural backdrops and coached us through the shots. When the wind blew, I worried my hair would blow off my head but smiled and said, "Cheese." I wanted my kids to have these memories. My hair stayed but my neck hurt from holding up that imaginary book.

For the rest of the day, I obsessively ran my hands through my hair. Each time, fingerfuls of hair tangled in my hands.

"Stop doing that," Mike insisted. I couldn't stop. I would call Nancy in the morning.

That night, I dreamt I woke up and found all my hair on my pillow. It was so real I immediately checked to see if my hair was still on my head. I planned to call Nancy that morning, but I didn't. I wasn't ready. That afternoon, as I pulled my debit card from the ATM, a large clump of hair landed on my arm. Instantly, I felt sick. I parked the car and made an appointment for the following afternoon. I called Darcie to check in at the center, but really I was upset and needed a friend. I told her about my hair.

"What happened?" Darcie asked, sounding distracted. I started to explain, but she cut me off.

"You knew this would happen, right?" she interrupted. "You made it through the wedding. You got your pictures. You're lucky your hair stayed that long." Her words stung.

"I've got to go. Kaley's mom is here," she said, and hung up the phone. She must have had a busy day.

* *

In a few hours, my hair would be gone. I dropped Kalea at school and planned to spend the morning with Kade. Mom called to say we needed milk. She didn't think I would want to stop after my hair appointment. She was right.

I pulled into the pharmacy side of Giant Eagle, closest to the milk aisle. I parked close to the door, walked straight back to the milk, and back to the front to check out. As I neared the register, I saw my friend Kelly. I wasn't sure I could handle seeing anyone.

"Jen!" she shouted. I hesitated, and turned around.

"How are you?" she asked.

"I have to get my hair shaved off today," I said, holding back sobs.

"That's okay," she said, her hands on my shoulders. "You are beautiful. You will still be beautiful." She gave me a hug. I fell into her and broke down in tears.

"Let me tell you a story," she said calmly, putting her groceries down on an empty check-out counter nearby. Kelly told me about a friend of hers, a busy mom diagnosed with cancer. She wondered how she was going to take care of her children, manage her job and the house. She didn't know if she could do it all while she was sick. Then, God put a message on her heart. He told her, "This is your time to be still."

"She worked so hard for years, doing everything for everyone," she said. "Her illness forced her to slow down. It was time to rest and

83

let others take care of her for a while. It was her time to be still. This is your time to be still, Jen." She gave me another hug, looked me in the eyes, and said, "It's going to be okay."

I let her words sink into my soul. *This was my time to be still.* Maybe she was right. When I prayed for God to help me off this crazy ride, cancer was not what I had in mind, but I had to get better. It was time to make my health a priority. Put myself first.

"This is my time to be still," I whispered to myself as I walked to the car. I thanked God for orchestrating my morning. Running out of milk and sending Kelly to the grocery store that morning to share that story.

Chapter Eleven

"I read you can get cancer from deodorant. What kind did you use? I also heard wearing a bra can cause cancer. Who knew? Oh, and eating food from the grill. That too. Did you perm your hair when you were a teenager? Geez. I will probably get cancer too. Oh well, we are all going to die from something, right?"

LADY IN THE CHECKOUT LINE AFTER SHE HEARD ME SAY I HAD
BREAST CANCER

I spent the morning with Kade, dropped him off at school, and drove to the salon. Nancy wasn't there, but I was greeted by Rachel, her assistant. She made me feel welcome, just like Nancy did. She was also gorgeous with beautiful long hair, perfect curls cascading down her back. It would be years before I could have hair like that again.

"Hop up in the chair," she said. "Is that your wig?" She pointed to the box in my hand. She pulled it out of the box and placed it on one of the creepy heads to brush it. I told her about my hair falling out in the shower and at the ATM machine.

"I'm sorry," she said. "Let's get this done and get you in your wig."

"I'm not ready for this," I said. "But do what you have to do."

She smiled sympathetically, running her hands through my hair, strands falling to the floor. She secured the cape around my neck. I took one last look in the mirror before I put my head down and closed my eyes. The clippers hummed as they glided over my scalp. I heard the metal blades cut through my hair and felt its weight land on my shoulders, slide down the cape and onto the floor. I shivered as my scalp met the cold air.

"It was just hair," everyone said. "It would grow back." But it was my hair. And it was gone. When the humming stopped, the room was quiet.

"You okay?" Rachel asked and squeezed my shoulders. I nodded, my head down and my eyes closed. Rachel brushed the stray hairs from my head and shoulders and removed the cape. I couldn't look.

"I will put the cap on first, and then the wig," she said, aware of my discomfort. The cap felt good on my cold bare scalp. As Rachel placed the wig on my head, I heard the clips snap.

"You want to be really careful about your hairline," she said. "Make sure you place it where your natural hair line was. If it is off, it is obvious you are wearing a wig."

"Okay," I said, wondering if I could do this on my own.

"You ready?" she asked, her hands resting on my shoulders. "It looks great!"

I opened my red, puffy eyes to my reflection and was pleasantly surprised. It looked like my hair, only longer. It looked perfect, actually.

"Do you like it?" Rachel asked. I nodded and watched her sweep up my hair in the dustpan.

"Can I save some of it?" I asked, wondering if that was weird. I thought maybe I should keep it for Mike? Did husbands keep locks of their dead wife's hair?

"Of course," said Rachel, placing a lock of hair in the sandwich bag I handed her from my purse. I came prepared.

"Thank you," I said as I got out of the chair, stealing a quick glance in the mirror. I walked upstairs and straight out the door. I didn't want to see the women upstairs getting their hair colored and styled. I got in my car, gripped the steering wheel, and looked in the rear-view mirror.

You have to get used to this, I said to myself in the rear-view mirror. *You have to be comfortable with this so the kids will be too.*

The center was near the salon. I called Allie to tell her I would pick up checks for deposit. She was standing outside when I pulled into the lot. She was the first person to see my wig.

"I love it!" Allie said. "I would never know that was a wig. That's amazing!"

I thanked her and took the envelope. She had no idea how much her kind and genuine words put me at ease. She was such a great employee, but an even better person and friend. I drove home, glancing in the mirror every few minutes. I was surprised by how natural it looked, but I grew more nervous as I got closer to home.

Would Mike like it? Would the kids?

Mike was at the sink when I walked into the kitchen.

"Well?" I said, turning for him to see the wig from all directions. I was so nervous but I pretended to be confident. More than anyone, I wanted Mike to like it.

"It looks good," he said, walking over to touch it. "You can't tell that is a wig. That is awesome." I sensed relief in his voice too.

"Thank you. I am going to take a nap until I have to get the kids," I said.

"You rest. I will pick up the kids today."

I went upstairs and called Darcie to see how things were going before I took a nap.

"All is well, here," she said. "I had to use petty cash to run to the store because we were totally out of paper towels."

"Oh no," I said. "I'm sorry. I ordered everything in the email. I don't remember seeing paper towels on the list."

"It's fine. You have a lot going on," she said with an edge, insinuating I made a mistake. I would place an extra order in the morning along with anything else she needed. When we got off the phone, I checked the email with last week's order. Paper towels weren't on the list.

I was making garlic bread to go with the spaghetti when Mike and the kids got home.

"Hi, Mommy," Kalea said. She didn't make eye contact when she walked into the kitchen. She didn't even look in my direction. Kade walked through behind her and went to the living room to play with his cars.

"Hi Kade," I said, "How was school?".

"Good," he said, lining up his cars.

I turned down the burner and followed Mike into his office.

"Why are the kids being weird?" I asked.

"I talked to them on the way home. I told them you were wearing your wig." I knew he wanted to save me from that difficult conversation but I wished he would have let me do it.

As the night went on, the kids never relaxed. They wouldn't look at me. They grew stiff when I hugged them. I had red circles under my eyes from wiping away tears through dinner.

"I'll give them baths tonight. I'll see what is going on," Mike offered.

They hated my wig. It was too long and I looked different. I called Nancy and ordered a shorter wig. I paid extra for faster shipping. When I put it on, I was happy and I looked like me. I couldn't wait for the kids to see it. When the kids came home that day, relief showed on their faces. They hugged me like they hadn't seen me in days.

I wore my wig until I went to bed, but left the wig on my nightstand. I set my alarm clock early. I didn't want the kids to see me without it. I didn't know if they could handle seeing me bald.

Although my head was shaved, it was a buzz cut. Very short hairs covered my scalp. When I removed my cap, it was full of tiny little hairs still falling out. One night, I pinched out the hairs in the shape of a heart on the side of my head. The next night, I made a star on the other. No one ever saw it but me. As more hair fell out, my scalp was itchy. Unbelievably itchy. It was terribly uncomfortable under my wig, but I couldn't scratch it. I used half a tube of hydrocortisone on my scalp one evening. I didn't know what else to do. A few days later, when all those little hairs fell out, the itching stopped and I had a perfectly smooth head.

I was used to wearing my wig, but I wanted to wear the purple knit cap when I was home. I had to talk to the kids. I took Kalea to my bedroom first.

"I like my wig, but it isn't very comfortable. I like to wear a cap sometimes too. Would you like to see my cap?" She nodded and sat on my bed while I went to the bathroom to put on my cap. I opened the door and Kalea looked at me, completely unaffected.

"I like your hat, Mommy," she said. "I like the wig better, but the hat is okay too."

I hugged her and thanked her for being so kind and so brave.

"I like purple, Mommy. It's okay," she said.

"Can you get your brother for me?" I asked. I put on my wig, hoping things went as well with Kade. When I told him about the cap, he looked confused. When I came out of the bathroom wearing it, he looked scared.

"What is under the hat, Mommy?" he asked, inspecting my head.

"I don't have any hair, Bud. My medicine is getting rid of my cancer, but it made my hair go away too. Remember when we talked about that?"

"Yes," he said. "Can I see?"

I knew he wasn't prepared to see my full bald head, so I pulled up the cap to show him a part of my scalp. He gasped. His eyes filled with terror. He screamed and sobbed, and ran away.

"Kade!" Kalea scolded. "You made Mommy cry!"

She ran after him as I melted onto the floor in a bald, sobbing mess. Kade looked at me like I was a monster. I washed my face, pulled myself together, and wore my cap downstairs. Kade glanced at me from across the room and put his head down. I went into the kitchen and left him alone while I washed a few dishes in the sink.

"Can I have more milk, Mom?" he asked a few minutes later, bringing me his cup.

"Sure, Bud," I said, pouring his milk. He took his cup and went over to the couch. "Want to watch Star with me, Mommy?"

"Absolutely!" I said as I joined him. That was it. He was fine. He just needed a little time.

* *

Mom offered to pick up the kids from school since Mike was out of town. It gave me an extra half an hour to rest before the kids got home. I woke up when I heard the garage door open. I only had two kids, but they sounded like twenty coming through the door, shedding shoes and coats and chattering about the school day.

Mom helped the kids empty their backpacks and I gave them a snack at the counter.

"I saw Darcie at the school. She didn't speak to me," Mom said.

"She probably didn't see you."

"She saw me," Mom said.

I was sure it was a misunderstanding. There must be an explanation.

I fell asleep again on the couch that evening and woke up with a burning stomach. I heard the kids giggling. Bath time. Mike had it covered.

I made a cup of tea. Chemo was kicking my butt, but things were going well. In some ways, I handled this cancer thing better than I thought. I put on my wig and a smile most of the time and muddled through the rest. I slept all the time. Mike and Mom did more than their fair share around the house. Darcie and Allie handled things at work. Neighbors stopped by with dinners and gift cards and surprises for the kids. I wasn't used to other people doing things for me but I was so very grateful. I didn't call cancer a gift, but it opened my eyes to the blessings in my life.

It was almost dark outside, but the autumn sun cast its final glow through the trees. Most of the leaves had fallen but a few held tight to the branches. I admired their strength and determination. They weren't ready to give up, choosing to hold on as long as they could. I wrapped my cold hands around my mug and took a sip of my hot tea. The warmth slid down my throat and deep into my soul.

"I'm with you, leaves. I'm holding on too."

Chapter Twelve

Standing with a group of people.
First person: *"Man, I couldn't believe my luck (insert situation here)*
Second person: *"But it's not like you have cancer...*
Me: *(Crickets)*

My second chemo treatment went better than the first. I was allowed to pull my curtain for privacy. I didn't notice any of the patients from last time. Mike dropped our bags and left to pick up lunch while Shari accessed my port. We chatted through my pre-meds during lunch. I made sure to pee before the Benadryl drip started so I could make a safe voyage to the bathroom with the IV pole. Mike worked when Benadryl knocked me out. I woke up when my nose caught fire and he drove me home. Chemo number two completed.

I stocked the freezer with more frozen fruit bars. My nurse suggested I take Claritin the day before, the day of, and the day after my shot to help with the side effects. She said the shot might not be as bad the second time around, but I wasn't taking any chances.

The Claritin worked, but I suffered a new side effect from chemo every day. I had stomach problems, bone and joint pain, dizziness, mouth sores, and itchy skin. All kinds of miserable. I was on the couch so much I felt like a cushion. I couldn't stand to walk barefoot. My feet were sensitive. I wore big fluffy socks at all times. My fingers were numb and tingly. My gums were raw and a new mouth sore formed on the inside of my cheek. I brushed my teeth and rinsed with Biotene. I caught a glimpse of myself in the mirror as I dried my face.

I didn't recognize my reflection. My skin was pasty white. My bald head was irritated and dry. My eyebrows and lashes were almost gone. I would have cried but I was too tired. I noticed the hair dryer, straightener, hairspray, styling products, and pile of hair ties on the bathroom counter, taunting me. It made me sad to look at them. I hadn't touched them in weeks and I wouldn't be able to use them for months. I threw all of the hair products in a basket and hid them in the back of the cabinet under the sink. I wiped the bare bathroom counter.

"That's better," I said. "Stupid cancer."

* *

Mike suffered from one of his migraines and went to bed early. I slept all day so I stayed downstairs. It was an emotional day. I sat on the couch and felt sorry for myself. I rarely spiraled to such a low point, but that night, I wallowed in my misery, watching reruns of old sit-coms. I started to doze off when I heard a thud and the pitter-patter of little feet coming down the steps. Kade appeared around the corner in his Buzz Lightyear pajamas. His blonde hair stood up in the back. Wrapped in a cocoon of blue blanket, the rest dragging along behind him, he ran to me in a blue blur and climbed onto the couch.

"I can't sleep," he said, melting into me. I should have walked him back to bed, but I couldn't. I welcomed the company. I wrapped him in his blanket and turned on Nick Junior. We giggled as we watched Star introduce the next show. Kade had the best belly laugh. I stroked his blond hair, his cheeks and his little nose. He was warm and snuggly and everything I needed. I held on to my little boy like a life preserver in the middle of the rough sea. He was tiny, but his presence was powerful. My body was battered but my heart was full.

God, let me be a mom a little longer. Let me finish the job you gave me. I want to live long enough so they will always remember me. I will remember this moment for the rest of my life – my little boy in his pajamas. His messy blond hair. His blue blanket. Thank you for sending my bundle of sweetness, my nighttime savior.

God sent that little boy downstairs because He knew I needed him.

Kade needed me too. We sat together for a couple of hours before I put us both to bed. We called it "Friday Night Sneaking Night" and it became a weekly routine. It was our lovely little secret.

* *

Kade was turning 6. Because he loved doughnuts so much, he wanted his birthday party at Krispy Kreme. He ran to the door and leaped inside. He pressed his little face and hands against the glass window and watched the doughnuts ride the conveyor belt under the glaze waterfall. I hoped he would always find joy in things like that. The little things.

"Are you the birthday boy?" the manager asked. Her name was Tina. Kade smiled a shy smile and nodded.

"We have a special gift for you!" Tina said, placing a Krispy Kreme hat on Kade's head and a 'birthday boy' sticker on his shirt. She gave him a new Krispy Kreme t-shirt too. Kade's mouth dropped open. He accepted it like it was a million dollars.

A few moments later, Darcie's husband Tom arrived with the kids. Kade ran to the door, hats in hand, to greet the kids.

"Where's Darcie?" I asked, "Everything okay?"

"Oh, yeah," Tom said, "She had some errands to run." I was disappointed as I was looking forward to seeing her.

The kids played a couple fun games. Tina lined them up and gave them a tour of the doughnut factory. Kade was living his best life. Before, I was too tired, too busy, and too worried about everything being perfect. This was the way it was supposed to be. Oh, how much I had been missing. But not anymore.

* *

October was our licensing month at the new center. The inspector scheduled our annual inspection on Halloween, one of the craziest days of the year at a child care center. Costumes, Halloween parades, games and snacks made for a hectic day. Since it was Halloween, I dressed up as a doctor, complete with a protective mask and gloves. Perfect! I promised Dr. Mendez and Mike I would stay in the office.

I handled all the paperwork and files. Darcie and the rest of the staff escorted our inspector through the classrooms for inspection.

I couldn't stop smiling under my protective mask. My life had been centered around doctor visits, blood draws, and chemo. It was great to experience what life was like before cancer.

When Darcie was with the inspector, I sat in the office. Mary walked in the office. She was great with the kids and the parents, professional and a hard worker. I told her all the time how happy I was to have her on my team.

"Hi, Mary!"

"Oh," stammered Mary, "I wasn't expecting to see you." She made a few copies but didn't look at me.

"I'm here for inspection. I miss you. How have you been?"

"I'm good," she said. "I better get downstairs. Party day!"

Mary was always so friendly. She must have had something going on at home.

Our inspection went well. I treated the staff to lunch to thank them for their hard work. I couldn't have done it without my team. They were amazing.

* *

I dropped off the supplies at the center. Darcie was busy so I left them outside the door. I made it to the school early and found a good parking spot. I worried I would have to park far away and be worn out before the program started. The kids were adorable. After the program, parents waited in the back for the kids to file out of the multi-purpose room and go back to their classrooms.

"Hi there!" said a dark-haired woman wearing too much makeup and clothes meant for someone ten years younger. She opened her arms to hug me. I couldn't remember her name.

"Hi" I said, awkwardly putting my arms around her.

"How are you?" she asked.

"I'm doing okay," I answered. "How are you?"

She told me about her grandmother's neighbor who had colon cancer, her last days in graphic detail.

"I helped with a fundraiser last year. I think it was a benefit for breast cancer. I wore a fabulous pink dress that night. And awesome shoes."

I smiled, not sure what to say.

"So, are you going to...you know..." she said, making a chopping motion across the front of her chest. I assumed she was asking if I was going to have a double mastectomy.

"That is the plan, but will focus on getting through chemotherapy first. One day at a time. All I can do, right?"

"You know, one of my sorority sisters had breast cancer a few years ago. It was terrible. Terrible! She lost all her hair and had to wear this awful wig. But she had that plastic surgery too. She is now a 34DD. She looks great. I am so jealous" she rattled on. "That's a perk, right?"

"I want to catch my daughter on the way back to class, I have to get home," I said.

"Okay," the woman said, waving goodbye. "Nice talking to you."

I was still shaking my head when I walked out the main door to the parking lot.

"I love your haircut," I heard someone say. Looking up, I saw my neighbor Stacy, walking toward me.

"Thank you," I said, and then whispered, "It's a wig." I always felt the need to explain.

Stacy looked confused.

"I have cancer. This is a wig," I said, even though she never asked. She was gracious, but I walked away feeling embarrassed.

Last week, I took Kalea to the bank to make a deposit. The teller complimented me on my hair. Before I could utter a simple thank you, Kalea got on her tip-toes and peered over the counter.

"It's a wig. My mommy has cancer," she said, then put the lollipop back in her mouth.

"I'm sorry," the teller said.

"It's okay. Thank you," I said, took the deposit slip and walked away. I discussed with Kalea about sharing personal business with others. I just did the same thing to Stacy. Ugh. I was almost 40 and still as backwards as I was in 7th grade.

On the way home, I called Allie to check in. We caught up on our personal lives and discussed enrollment. I pulled in my driveway and needed to get Kade ready for school.

"I better go. I will check in with you tomorrow."

"One more thing," she said. "How are things going at the other center? I call Darcie every week or so to see if she needs anything. She doesn't say much."

"Things are good," she said. "Maybe she feels intimidated by you, since I sing your praises all the time."

We laughed and then Allie had to go. Someone was at the door.

* *

I walked to the mailbox and heard someone calling my name. Stacy was walking down the sidewalk, a casserole dish in her hands.

"I made you a lasagna. You can heat it or freeze it and eat it when you want," she said. "I'll carry it for you." I grabbed the mail and something from the paper box and followed her to my door.

"That was so sweet of you, but you didn't have to do that. Thank you so much."

"I had no idea you were sick. I would have made something sooner. Let me know if you need anything," said Stacy. I thanked her again and went inside. I had only met Stacy a couple of times. She found out I was sick and made my family a meal. I thought about the woman from the school talking about her grandmother, her fabulous pink dress, and her friend's boob job.

People really were different, weren't they?

I went through the mail and saw the postcard was from another neighbor. Kathy was hosting a jewelry party next weekend. I had been feeling better and an afternoon of socializing might do me some good. I was in a much better place than I was for Kari's party. It was nice to add something other than a doctor appointment to my calendar.

That night, my friend Heidi called me to catch up. Her neighbor, Debbie, was diagnosed with stage 4 metastatic breast cancer. Debbie was grocery shopping and tripped on a curb. Believing she broke her arm, she went to the hospital. She found out she had breast cancer that metastasized to 205 of her 206 bones. I didn't know breast cancer did that. Heidi, who was a nurse, told me breast cancer typically spreads to the bones, lungs, liver, or brain. Unfortunately, Debbie's breast cancer wasn't discovered until it had already metastasized. She was diagnosed with stage 4 de novo, meaning her cancer had already spread by the time it was found. Praise God my cancer was detected before it spread. Heidi asked me to reach out to Debbie. I was glad I did. We became fast friends.

"It is very hard to vent sometimes simply because if you are not experiencing this, you just don't know how to respond. I just want to scream sometimes, even though I know it won't help. I have been at this for 3 ½ years already but not giving in to it. I got this and so do you!" Debbie wrote.

She had been through so much and was such a strong person. She endured one treatment after another only to find out she had progression. The treatments were harsh and the side effects were many.

"This journey has been endless and I hope to see a light at the end of the tunnel soon," she said. I hoped she did too.

It was refreshing to talk to someone who understood. We stayed up late messaging about everything from chemo side effects to stupid things people said. Debbie understood. We talked about some pretty deep stuff and some sad subjects, but she was always so positive. I got excited when I saw her green light was on in messenger.

* *

The morning of the jewelry party, I woke up excited to have something to do. Getting dressed up and putting on a little makeup made me feel better than I had in a long time. Happy to do something normal, I did not want to think about cancer today.

I walked outside and up the hill. Kathy lived in the neighborhood, but it seemed like miles away. It took my time. Slow and steady. It was amazing how much I saw when I slowed down and looked around. It was cold outside, but the birds were singing. The sky was blue and the clouds were spread across the sky like marshmallow fluff. The breeze picked up some leaves, swirled them in the air and dropped them in a pile next to a mailbox post. The sun broke through the clouds and its rays shined down and warmed my face. There was a time when I would have missed all of that.

I made it to Kathy's house and rang the bell.

"I'm so glad you could make it!" she said, opening the door. "How are you doing?"

"I'm doing well. It's a good day today!"

"Well, I am happy it is a good day!' she said and showed me to the kitchen.

I put some fruit and a few crackers on a plate, and carefully filled my cup with ice and water. My fingers were so numb, I was dropping things and getting so clumsy. I didn't want to make a mess. I took my time but felt someone behind me. I hurried to get out of the way.

"Hi, Jennifer," said Tracy, looking at me with those pity eyes.

"Hi, Tracy. How are you?"

"How are you?" she said, eyes laser-focused on me. "I am so sorry you are going through all of this."

My heart sank. I didn't want to talk about cancer.

"I'm okay," I answered. "Hanging in there. How are the kids?"

"They are fine. Busy with their advanced classes. When do you have treatment?" she asked, staring intently at my wig.

"Every three weeks. I go next week for Round 3." I started to walk away.

"Is that a wig? So, you lost all your hair?"

She asked questions about my wig, my hair, my surgery, and a hundred other things.

"I'm going to check out the jewelry," I interrupted her and turned to go. I didn't want to be rude but I didn't want to talk about cancer. I looked forward to today and she was ruining it.

The other women gathered around the table. We engaged in light, friendly conversation about jewelry, weather, and how quickly the holidays were approaching, but nothing about cancer.

I ate fruit that wasn't frozen, I chose a pretty bracelet the color of the sky; and for a few hours, I was a person, not a patient.

Chapter Thirteen

*(After explaining how badly my throat hurt after chemo
to a woman in the grocery aisle.)*
*"You mean you couldn't even eat? I need to lose some weight.
Maybe I should ask my doctor to give me some chemo?"*

Chemo #3!" Pam said, as we followed her back to the chemo lab.

"Halfway there," I said. Dr. Mendez prescribed six rounds of chemo.

I settled into my recliner and wrapped myself in Mom's pink blanket. The chemo lab was busy, but Pam sat with me for a little while. Dr. Mendez ordered a decrease in my dosage because of the numbness in my hands and feet. I worried it wouldn't work as well.

"It's like this," Pam said. "We want to get rid of the cancer with as little collateral damage as possible."

An alarm beeped somewhere across the room and Pam left to check on her patient. I asked her to pull my curtain before she left. Alone for a few minutes in my chemo chair, I closed my eyes and prayed.

God, thank you for walking me through this chemo. Thank you for the doctors and the nurses who have been so wonderful. Thank you for the amazing people you have placed in my life to support me. I ask for healing and for protection from the harsh chemo meds. I feel myself growing weaker with each treatment. I'm worried about how much my body can endure. Give me the strength to keep going, even when I don't feel like it. I trust in you. Amen.

Thanksgiving was next week. My chemo schedule worked out well. The terrible sore throat came on day two and would be gone in time for

Thanksgiving dinner. I didn't want to eat a frozen fruit bar instead of turkey and mashed potatoes. So much to be thankful for and I didn't want cancer to mess up my holiday.

When we got home that afternoon, I was wiped out. A neighbor dropped off dinner. When the neighbors asked to start a meal train, I told them it wasn't necessary. I didn't need meals or rides to chemo or doctor appointments. After talking to a friend, I agreed to accept meals on treatment days. My neighbor Erin arranged it and it was such a big help.

"I feel so uncomfortable accepting help," I said to my friend Barb. "We can manage. People keep asking what they can do. I don't know what to say."

"Jen, people want to help. They can't cure cancer. They can't make you better, but they can cook you a meal. Let them. Don't take away their opportunity to bless you."

She was right. I kept that in mind when people asked if they could make a meal or take the kids for a while. I knew I would do the same for them. I was learning to accept help. I didn't have to do it alone.

"Are we going to do the tree after dinner?" Kalea asked as we sat down to a lovingly prepared meal that night. She was searching through her rice for every pea she could find.

On November 1st, we started the "Collins Thankful Tree". Every day, we wrote something we were thankful for on one of the construction board leaves and added it to the poster board tree. Kalea wrote "Grandma" and Kade wrote "doughnuts". That night, I chose a bright orange leaf and wrote "Done with Chemo #3".

The next few days were rough. My body ached so badly, Mike had to drive me to the cancer center for my shot. My throat was sore the first night after chemo and showed no signs of subsiding. I was tired of eating frozen fruit bars, my fingers were numb, and my feet hurt. I got winded walking a few steps. I slept during the day and stayed up most of the night. Those late nights alone were the hardest.

Because I didn't feel well and Dr. Mendez told me to avoid crowds whenever possible, we stayed home a lot through my treatment. The kids were used to going into the city or to local events on weekends. We rarely stayed home.

"Why don't you put on a skit for me?" I suggested. I told them to think of a story, find some costumes, and perform for me. They hurried upstairs. A while later, they returned to the family room in costume. Kalea was dressed in a pink princess gown and shiny white gloves. Kade wore black cat ears, a fuzzy tail, and painted-on whiskers.

I watched their imaginative performance about a princess and her naughty cat. They did an amazing job. They were both so creative and I was happy they worked together with no fighting.

"Bravo!" They took a bow, big cheesy grins on their faces.

"Did you like the skit, Mommy?" Kalea asked as she sat next to me on the couch.

"I loved it!"

"Yay!" they said as they took off to change with a confidence I hadn't seen in a while.

* *

Tomorrow was Thanksgiving Day. Mom and I went shopping the week before to get everything we needed. I put the turkey and all the fixings in the cart, wondering if I would be able to eat them. A week out of chemo, I was still tired, but my sore throat was gone. I had never been that excited about Thanksgiving.

We celebrated Thanksgiving Eve with a movie night. The kids chose *Elf*. We pulled out blankets and pillows and snuggled together. Buddy the Elf had just arrived in New York City when I noticed that Mike and both kids were sleeping. I watched the rest of the movie by myself.I slept most of the day so I was wide awake. I took advantage of a rare burst of energy and got a head start on Thanksgiving dinner.

I prepped the turkey, peeled and cut the potatoes, and made the sweet potato casserole. It was late, but I kept going while I had the energy. I set the large mixing bowl on the counter. When I pulled Mom's old rolling pin from the drawer, Kade sat up in the family room and ran to the kitchen.

"Can I help?" he asked. I glanced at the clock. It was so late, but why not?

"Sure, Bud. Want to help me make the noodles?"

I pulled a chair over to the kitchen counter. Kade helped scoop and measure the flour, crack the eggs, and make the dough.

"Do you want to cut them?"

"Yes!" he said. I handed him the pizza cutter and he pushed it across the dough. The noodles were all different sizes. There was a time that would have driven me crazy.

"Awesome job, Little Man!".

It was almost midnight when we finished. I washed the mixing bowl and Kade wiped the counter. We woke Mike and Kalea and we all went to bed. It felt like Christmas Eve.

I woke up in a fog of fatigue and random aches and pains. I put the turkey in the oven and we watched the parade. Later, Mom and the kids helped me with the rest of dinner. I looked around the table at my family and thought about Dad. He loved holidays. He cooked big family meals; pouring his love into every dish. Sometimes, he didn't even feel like eating by the time he was done, but he was happy just to sit at the table. All that mattered was that his family was together. I understood how he felt back then. My cup runneth over.

* *

When I went to my next appointment, I was struggling. Dr. Mendez was concerned. My tumor didn't shrink much since the last chemo treatment. He feared we reached a plateau with my chemotherapy.

"There is a point when the benefits from chemo no longer outweigh the toll it takes on the body. I fear we are approaching that point," said Dr. Mendez. As difficult as it was, I did not want to stop chemo unless it was necessary.

"We will make a decision about chemo #5 at your next blood work appointment. See how this one goes," he said.

My 4th chemo was uneventful. Mike and I talked and ate lunch during my pre-meds. The thin IV pole rolled with me to the bathroom before my Benadryl drip. Then Mike worked on his laptop while I slept until Cytoxan burned my nose. We had this chemo thing down.

"Merry Christmas," Pam said and hugged me as we gathered our things. "You keep doing what you are doing. You got this." My next treatment #5 was on December 26th, the day after Christmas.

"Not too excited about coming here the day after Christmas,"

I said.

"We will be here and we will make it fun. You'll be alright."

"Cancer sucks," I said.

"I know," said Pam. "One step closer to done, right?"

After wishing Pam a Merry Christmas, I packed my bag and Mike drove us home. Christmas music played on the radio. I was usually up for some *Jingle Bells* or *White Christmas*, but not today. I changed the station.

Phillip Phillips' "Home" really was my chemo theme song.

Chemo #4 hit me pretty hard. I was in a lot of pain. I lived on frozen fruit bars for a week. My feet were numb and ached at the same time. My fingertips felt like balloons and I could barely hold a pen. I spent more time sleeping than anything else. I tried to see that light at the end of the tunnel Debbie mentioned, but I could barely keep my eyes open.

Although my Christmas spirit waxed and waned, we turned the house into the Christmas Wonderland like we did every year. While the kids dreamed of sugarplums, I tried to keep up with the holiday rush. During an online Black Friday sale, I purchased season tickets for Kennywood, a local amusement park, for next summer. The deal included free passes to their first ever Holiday Lights celebration. Pittsburgh was experiencing temperatures in the upper 50's in mid-December. I was feeling a little better so we took advantage of the mild temperatures and packed up the kids.

We emerged from the entrance tunnel to find our summer destination decked out in Christmas lights and decorations. Holiday music flowed through the speakers and the park was transformed into a Christmas village. From the stands that served popcorn and pretzels in the summertime, we ordered hot chocolate and fresh cookies. We watched an artist carve a reindeer from an ice block. The kids wrote a letter and dropped it in a mailbox for Santa. We took a picture with a snowman and checked out a huge, miniature train display. There was so much to do and we did it all.

As we rounded the bend, the carousel sat at the bottom of the hill covered in lights and decorated with wreaths and bows. The carousel was my favorite. Riding a carousel brought back childhood memories. I rode that same carousel as a little girl. The music started and we began to spin. It was magic. The lights twinkled, the smell of cinnamon hung in the air, and my kids' giggles filled me with all the good cheer. It was the first time that season I let myself enjoy Christmas.

I was mad that cancer was ruining my holiday. I wasn't looking forward to Christmas because everything was different. I didn't have enough energy to do all the things we did at Christmastime.

What was I really missing? Christmas parties? Crowded shopping malls? Chaotic events? I was only missing the parts of Christmas I didn't enjoy anyway. We watched Christmas movies. We drank hot chocolate with marshmallows and candy canes. We baked and decorated cookies. I wasn't missing anything. Christmas had been there all along. I almost missed it being angry and miserable. I saddled a carousel horse on a balmy night in Pittsburgh and finally found the Christmas Spirit.

* *

My stomach was in knots as the elevator doors closed. I would find out this morning if I had to come back the day after Christmas for chemo #5. If I needed six chemo treatments to get rid of this cancer, stopping at 4 made me nervous.

"So, what do you think, Jen?" Dr. Mendez asked, sitting back in his chair, his cheerful Christmas socks peeking out from under his pant legs.

"I'm not sure," I said.

"Jen, the tumor isn't shrinking anymore. Your counts are down. You have fatigue, some neuropathy that can't be reversed, you look pretty run down. I think we should stop."

"So no more chemo?" I asked, glancing at Mike. "Is that okay?"

"Yes. I prescribed six rounds, but that was as tolerated. I am happy with four, especially since you are opting for a double mastectomy. We will push up your surgery to January or February when you are ready. Your body needs some time to recover. You can consult with Dr. Barton and your plastic surgeon."

"So no more chemo? I'm done?" I wasn't sure how to feel about that. Part of me wanted to jump out of my chair, but I didn't have the energy. Was I giving up too quickly?

"No more chemo. Go home and have a Merry Christmas." Mendez hugged me and shook Mike's hand.

Mike turned toward me, more relaxed than I had seen him in a while.

"Let's go home," he said.

As the elevators closed, I realized I didn't have to sit in that recliner again. No more thin IV poles. No more Benadryl. No more frozen fruit bars. No more fatigue! No chemo on December 26th! Praise the Lord! Hallelujah! What a Christmas gift!

* *

I set the box of tissues next to me on the couch and pulled a second blanket on top of me. The unwrapped presents were piled up and pushed back under the tree. We visited family on Christmas Eve so we could spend a quiet Christmas Day at home. The kids played with their toys, we had a small family dinner, and relaxed for the rest of the day.

After putting the kids to bed, Mike stood in front of me, his hands on his hips, looking concerned.

"You are miserable, aren't you?" he asked.

He sat down, tucking the blankets tightly around me. I woke up on Christmas morning with a terrible cold. I snuggled next to him and we watched *The Holiday*, one of my favorite movies. The perfect end to a special day. I had a cold on Christmas, but I didn't have chemo in the morning. Best Christmas ever.

Chapter Fourteen

After discussing my treatment plan, including chemo, bilateral mastectomy, reconstruction, and radiation with a colleague... "That's awesome! You get a free boob job."

I was up late working on some bookkeeping when Debbie messaged me. She was starting a new clinical trial she called 'the smart bomb'. We prayed this one would work. She needed some good news.

"This one will target the cancer cells only and give me a better chance. I am anxious about this one. It can cause liver toxicity so they have to be careful."

"Continued prayers, my friend," I wrote to her. "Get some rest and keep me posted."

It was terrible that the drugs that fought cancer caused so much other damage. As I signed off for the night, an invitation to a kids' birthday party popped up on Facebook. Kalea would love to go but I couldn't RSVP until I heard from Dr. Barton about my surgery date.

I would have a bilateral mastectomy with immediate reconstruction in a couple of weeks. The surgeon would inject a dye into the tumor area before surgery. The lymph nodes affected by the dye would be removed and checked for cancerous cells. The double mastectomy included removing all tissue from the chest area. Expanders would be inserted behind muscles pulled from the chest wall. These muscles were flat and had to be stretched over time. After I healed from the initial surgery, the plastic surgeon would inject fluid into the expanders, increasing their size and stretching the chest wall muscles.

These 'fill' appointments would occur every 2 weeks until the expanders reached the desired size. An additional surgery would replace the expanders with traditional implants. It was a long and somewhat barbaric process.

While Allie kept everything running smoothly at the first center, things were unsettled at the new center. Darcie cut back on her hours to be home more with her family. We hired new staff as enrollment increased. Not everyone got along. It was difficult to run the center when I couldn't be there. The stress and worry over the center was overwhelming at times.

* *

When I met with my plastic surgeon, Dr. Patterson, we chatted about cancer and the effect it had on patients. She had seen many breast cancer patients over the years. Although cancer was hard on the patient, it took a toll on everyone around them. Divorce rates were high after cancer. Relationships suffered.

"I have a friend who sort of disappeared. I think she is afraid something is going to happen to me. She dropped off a gift basket when I was first diagnosed, but I haven't heard from her since," I explained. "I understand, but it still hurts."

"Yes, that is normal. People don't know how to handle it so they just drop off the face of the earth. Sadly, you will lose a lot of friends when you go through something like this," she said.

Later, I talked to Mike about our conversation.

"That doesn't make sense. People shouldn't leave when you need them most. I don't expect them to heal me or make me feel better, but I just want to know they are there," I rambled.

"People don't know how to handle it," said Mike.

"I think people don't want to bother me, assuming I am sleeping or sick. I wish they would still call, or even text. If I am sleeping or sick, I won't answer. I'll still be happy to get the message and I will call back when I can. And why do people stop inviting you to things when you get sick? I may not be able to go but let me make that decision. Having cancer is lonely. People move on with their lives and leave you behind. They forget about you."

"Then let them move on. Real friends don't leave," Mike said.

"She said that marriages are at risk too. She has seen so many marriages ruined by cancer. When her patients come back for a follow-up, it isn't uncommon for them to tell her they got a divorce. It's sad."

"You don't have to worry about that," Mike said. "I'm not going anywhere."

"I know," I said. "Losing friends? Divorce? Someone gets cancer and they have to worry about losing friends and being left by their spouses? Sometimes, it is too much."

* *

I made a cup of tea and sat in the morning room to watch the snow fall. We got a few inches last night and another couple of inches were expected today. The bare branches on the hill were frosted with fluffy snow. Big flakes twirled down from the winter sky. Some fell straight down; set on their earthly target. Others spiraled with the wind, free falling then floating back up toward the sky, in no hurry to reach their destination.

If I were a snowflake, I would be the one that fell straight down. Get from Point A to Point B as efficiently as possible. I wasn't brave enough to ride the wind. I worried too much to enjoy the trip. I watched the snowflakes for a while longer, focused on the dancing ones, swirling and looping through the air. I envied them. I spent the first 39 years of my life falling straight down, too afraid to veer off course. I was organized. I got things done. I took my work planner to my oncology appointments. Why did I do that?

I was learning though. The quicker I got to where I was going, the more I missed along the way. I couldn't fit cancer into the squares of my calendar. I didn't want to fit life into those squares either. Like those snowflakes, I had to trust that as *topsy-turvy* as the path may be, I would land on solid ground when the time was right.

Lord, I need your guidance. I need your strength. I am tired and I am weak. I give it all to you. You made a way through every obstacle, every stumbling block. When I didn't see a way, You made one. You have been so faithful. You tell me to cast my fears on you, so I do that today. Take it from me. Take all of it. The cancer, the center, my family. I will keep my eyes on you, knowing I will be okay. I trust you, Lord.

I finished my tea and put my cup in the sink. I would remember those snowflakes and learn to be okay with *topsy-turvy.*

* *

I was about to run some errands when Dr. Barton's office called. My surgery was scheduled for January 18th. I marked it on the calendar and told Mike so he could request off from work. We could make it to the birthday party. In a couple weeks, the surgery would be over. One step closer to being cancer-free.

So focused on getting rid of the cancer, I never thought about losing my breasts. Even with reconstruction, I would never look the same again. It was sad, scary, and unfair. Mike said it didn't matter to him, but I worried he would feel differently when it was over. I worried he would no longer find me attractive. I was angry my body turned against me. Cutting off the offending parts seemed the right thing to do; a weird kind of justice. But losing a part of me, a womanly part of me, was hard. I feared cancer returning, so I wanted it done. January 18th. I marked it on my calendar.

* *

I called Christi once the date was set. She went through the same surgery so I called to talk about her experience with surgery.

"It was hell," she said.

"Hmmm," I said, not sure what to say.

"Hey, I told you I would always tell you the truth," Christi said.

It wasn't easy to hear but she gave awesome advice the doctors never did. I found a robe with inside pockets to hold the drains after surgery so the kids didn't see them. She warned me they were disgusting and uncomfortable. When I showered, I could use a plastic lanyard to clip them out of the way. Christi suggested oversized button-down shirts for easier dressing. I bought a couple sports bras that closed in the front. I pulled extra pillows from the linen closet to prop me up on the bed. I moved everyday items onto the counter from upper shelves because I would not be able to reach above my head for a while.

I prepared as much as I could before my surgery with Christi's help. She was an angel and my rock. I was so thankful God placed her in my life.

* *

When we arrived at the birthday party, Kalea immediately ran off with the kids. Most of the adult guests hung out in the kitchen. One other couple was seated in the family room. I recognized the woman from school. She sat on the love seat and her younger son was sleeping on her lap. Her husband sat near the fireplace in a recliner. There were crutches lying on the floor beside him.

"It's nice to meet you. I'm Susan. I see you all over the place," she said.

She was right. Over the last couple of months, I saw her in parking lots and grocery stores frequently. We saw each other at parent pick-up at the school too, but never officially introduced ourselves. Mike and her husband Giuseppe watched a game on television and chatted about sports and weather. Susan and I talked about spelling homework and first grade happenings. She asked if I was going to an upcoming school event.

"No, I can't. I have my surgery scheduled next week," I blurted out, not thinking. Ugh. *Why did I say that?*

"What kind of surgery?" she asked. A double mastectomy wasn't the typical knee replacement or shoulder surgery. I still didn't know how to bring it up in conversation.

"I have breast cancer," I said. "I went through chemo but next is a double mastectomy with reconstruction. That is scheduled for the 18th."

"What?" she asked. "You have cancer?" I couldn't read the look on her face. *Way to go, Jen. You made things awkward.*

"This is a wig. My hair is starting to grow but I still have to wear it," I said. The words kept spewing from my mouth even though I kept telling myself to stop talking. *Go ahead, Jen. You're doing a great job of making her uncomfortable.*

She had no idea I wore a wig. I was afraid I said too much. I'm sure

111

dropping the cancer bomb on someone the first time you met was inappropriate. I figured we would exchange a hesitant 'hi' the next time we saw each other at pick-up and never speak again.

I was pleasantly surprised when later that night, I received a friend request from her. Maybe I didn't scare her off after all. Susan was funny and it was easy to talk to her. We had a lot in common. We found out quickly that we were both Christians, over-protective moms, and empaths. And we were both the direct opposite of fancy. We chatted almost every day and made plans to get our families together for dinner after my surgery. I immediately felt close to her. While a lot of my friends seemed to step back since my diagnosis, Susan stepped up. We became fast friends, and I really needed a friend.

Chapter 15

"Although the world is full of suffering, it is also full of the overcoming of it."

HELEN KELLER

My chemo bag was still on the floor in my bedroom. I packed my robe, clothes, my pink blanket, and my Bible for the hospital. I took a long hot shower. It would be days before I could get another one. I dropped the towel and looked at my reflection in the mirror.

"You will never look like this again," I whispered to my reflection. I wasn't really sad. I was numb. Indifferent. Maybe it was denial. I took one last look and put on my pajamas. I set the alarm and climbed into bed, fluffed my pillow and pulled up the covers. I couldn't sleep.

What if something went wrong? What if I didn't come home? I checked on the kids. I watched them sleep. The next few months would be challenging, and I hoped they would be alright. I kissed them lightly on their foreheads and walked back to the bedroom.

I'm scared, God. I am afraid of the anesthesia, the surgery, the recovery, and reconstruction. All of it. Please calm my nerves and give me the strength to get through this. Guide the doctors' hands. Look after my family and bring comfort to Mike and Mom. Protect the kids. Thank you for all you have done for me and for walking with me through every step. I know you will be with me tomorrow.

I pulled the covers around me and went to sleep.

* *

We pulled out of the driveway at 5:30 in the morning. Friends texted prayers and well wishes on the way to the hospital. I reached for
Mike's hand. He wouldn't be sitting next to my beige recliner today.
He would wait in a room decorated in mauve or mint green on padded
chairs under framed prints of front porches or sailboats. For hours,
he would sit amongst strangers while doctors split me wide open on
a cold, hard table. I shuddered and pushed those thoughts from my
mind. It was okay. I would sleep through it. When I woke up, it would
be over, and Mike would be right beside me. He was *always* right beside me.

Oh no! Mike would be right beside me. I wore my wig to the hospital
but my white and purple cap was in my bag. They wouldn't allow me
to wear it in surgery. When they called me back to get changed and
prepped, I asked the nurse if I could wear a blue surgical cap on my
head during surgery.

"Please. My hair is growing back in but it looks absolutely awful.
I know it is silly and vain but I don't feel comfortable. I can't wear my
purple knit cap but will they let me wear one of those blue surgical
caps?"

She left and returned with two surgical caps. I placed my knit cap
in the clear bag marked "Patient Belongings" and put the two caps on
my head.She would mention it to the surgical nurse when I got to the
operating room. She brought Mike back to see me but he barely sat
down when the attendant rolled up to the door.

"Your chariot awaits, my dear," said the man in scrubs, motioning
to the bed.

I climbed onto the bed as the nurse ran down the hall.

"I talked to the O/R nurse. We're all set," she said, giving me the
thumbs up. I didn't have time to explain to Mike. We said, "I love you"
and Mike kissed me goodbye. As they wheeled me away, I held onto his
hand until I had to let go.I didn't want to let go.

* *

I woke up in a hospital room. I didn't feel pain, but I was afraid to
move. My hospital gown was open in the front, blood-tinged bandages
wrapped my chest. Five tubes, two on one side and three on the other

hung from my body. Drains. Yuck.

Dr. Patterson entered the room and stood at my bedside.

"Hey, there," she said resting her hand on my arm. "Everything went well. It took a little longer than we expected, but it is all over. Dr. Barton was pleased with the double mastectomy, and then I placed the expanders. The chest muscles were very tight, so I was unable to inject any fluid into the expanders. We will do that slowly when you heal."

I couldn't do any more than nod.

"I talked to Mike. He can share more information when you are ready," she said, "I will check in with the nurse tonight and I will be back to see you tomorrow. You get some rest."

Dr. Patterson turned to leave, but turned back.

"I talked to Mike. You definitely have a good one there. He is a good husband. I saw the concern on his face this morning. He was really worried, and listened to every word I said. Then I saw the relief on his face after the surgery. It was a long day for him too. He loves you. He's a keeper. I just wanted to say that to you. Now you get some rest."

I was still groggy from the anesthesia, but I heard Dr. Patterson loud and clear. I already knew Mike was a great husband, but I appreciated hearing it from her. I dozed off for a while until a nurse entered the room to check my vitals and empty my drains.

"Would you mind getting my purple cap out of my bag?" I asked the nurse.

"Sure," she said. She opened the cabinet and pulled out my bag. She handed me the cap, but I couldn't move my arms.

"Let me help you," she said, removing the surgical caps. I could barely lift my head, I was so weak.

"There," she said, gently sliding the white and purple cap over my head. I was embarrassed but the nurse was so kind. Nurses really are wonderful people.

Mike came in a few minutes later. He did look relieved. He pulled a chair next to my bed and held my hand. We didn't say much. We didn't have to. He stayed a while, but I was sleepy from the anesthesia and couldn't stay awake.

"Why don't you go home to the kids?" I suggested. "You have been here all day. The kids will want to see you and I am sure Mom could use the break." He didn't want to leave me, but he went home. There was nothing he could do for me and I planned to sleep off this anesthesia. He kissed my forehead and left for home.

Except when the nurses came in to take vitals and empty drains, I slept through the night. In the morning, one of the nurses turned on the television and put the remote near the end of the bed. *Hoarders* was on. I watched it for a little while, too tired to find something else. I fell asleep and woke up to another episode of *Hoarders*. It was a marathon weekend. I wanted to turn the channel, but I couldn't move to reach the remote.

Around dinnertime, a nurse entered the room and introduced herself.

"Hi there. I'm Patty. Ready to get out of that bed?" she asked. She didn't wait for an answer. She pulled a chair close to the bed. Before I could prepare, she slid her hand behind my back to help me sit up. A raw, burning pain shot through my chest.

"Take a minute," she instructed. "Then we will swing your legs around."

I waited just a few seconds and moved my legs on my own. The pain ripped through me again.

"Take your time. Then, I will help you stand."

I waited for the pain to lessen and she helped me stand. I leaned on her, feeling faint from the pain. So much pain.

"I'm going to throw up!" I yelled. A wave of nausea suddenly came over me. The nurse helped me sit down on the bed and grabbed one of those kidney-shaped pink pans.

"Use this if you need it," she said setting it on the bedside table.

I took a few deep breaths hoping the feeling would pass. I could think of nothing more painful than using all the muscles it would take to throw up right then. Thankfully, a few moments later, the feeling passed.

"Probably just from the pain," the nurse said. "Let's try again."

I stood up on my own, a little more steady this time. Another wave came over me and there was nothing I could do. Instinctively, I put my hand to my mouth, and the motion sent pain down the right side of my chest. The nurse held up the pink pan to my mouth and I let it go. She grabbed another pan as the first filled with clear liquid. The pain made me catch my breath and moan in pain. Every wretch felt like I was tearing myself open from the inside out. I sat down, waiting for the pain to subside.

"That was from the anesthesia," the nurse said as she cleaned up the mess.

"I'm so sorry," I stammered, embarrassed and shaking from the pain.

"No need to be sorry," Patty said. "It happens."

She helped me back to bed. "You will probably start to feel better now after you got that out of you. You were in surgery for a long time. That was a lot of anesthesia."

She was right. After a few minutes, the nausea was gone. I was still in terrible pain but I was more alert than I had been since surgery.

"You want to try something easy for dinner?" she asked. I was hungry. I hadn't eaten since the night before my surgery. The nurse brought me chicken soup that was mostly broth, crackers, and ginger ale. I finished everything, but the ginger ale. I didn't like ginger ale.

After my next dose of pain meds, I moved a little easier. I found the remote and turned the channel. No more *Hoarders*. When Mike called, he sounded terrible. He wanted to come visit, but he didn't want to get me sick.

"Stay home and rest," I said. "I'm going to do the same. I'll see you tomorrow. Love you."

I slept better that night. They removed my catheter and my oxygen in the morning. I walked myself to the bathroom. I felt like I had to pee, but I couldn't go. That happened all morning. The nurse was concerned. I had to pee in a measured insert in the toilet and notify the nurse every time I went. If I didn't go, the catheter would be reinserted.

She thought moving might do the trick. She helped me with my robe and walked me out into the hallway. We walked one lap around the nurse's station. Then another.

"Can we go around again?" I asked. "I feel good."

Patty said I could walk a few more laps, but warned me not to overdo it. She had no idea who she was talking to. I walked another couple of laps. I was halfway around the nurse's station for the third time when I felt warmth running down my leg. Was this really happening? I was bald and bandaged, wearing a fluffy pink robe over a gown that exposed my backside—and I was peeing myself! Now that was an all time low. I hobbled as quickly as I could toward my room, feeling more drips with every step.

Patty popped out of a nearby room. "Look at you go!" she cheered. A second later, her smile disappeared.

"I think I'm peeing!" I yelled to her. She looked down and her face grew pale. I followed her eyes and had to turn my whole body to look behind me. Drops of blood trailed behind me as far back as I could see. I started crying. The nurse ushered me into the room and onto the bed. She tried to stay calm, but I saw the fear on her face.

"What happened?" I asked. "Did my incision open?" The nurse didn't answer. She was frantically trying to find the source of the blood.

Patty stepped back, lowered her chin to her chest, and chuckled. She approached the bedside to look me in the face.

"You are not going to believe this. I think you just started your period!"

Seriously? I hadn't had a period since September, the month before I started chemo. Dr. Mendez said it might never come back. Then today, of all days, my period decided to make a triumphant return.

Patty cleaned me up and brought me one of those mommy diaper pads they give you after you have a baby. What a sight I must have been. Peach fuzz and black spindly hairs hid under a purple and white knit cap. Blood soaked bandages encased my newly flattened chest. Bulbous drains dangled from my person. I had to ask a nurse to check my pee. And now I had to wear a diaper. Talk about a humbling experience.

Cancer sucked, but Patty was a saint.

* *

Dr. Patterson stopped early the next morning.

"I heard you had an exciting day yesterday," she said, smiling sympathetically. "You would be surprised how often that happens when women have surgery.

"How embarrassing! I was hoping my period would never come back."

"It's fine. Happens all the time. I wanted to talk to you about something. I'm not sure about sending you home." She asked if Mike was prepared to help me at home. She mentioned arranging a visiting nurse.

"We can manage," I said. "He wasn't feeling well yesterday, but we should be okay." Dr. Patterson looked worried.

"You know, I think I am going to keep you one more day. You can get a little more rest. We can decrease your pain meds before you go home. That gives Mike some more time to get better. I don't want to risk you getting sick on top of everything else."

I wanted to protest. I wanted to go home, but she was right.

"I get it," Mike said, over the phone after she left. "The kids are going to be disappointed. We were excited to bring you home."

I was glad he felt better. He planned to take the kids somewhere fun. I spent the afternoon walking laps around the nurses station, sitting up in a chair, and dozing on and off. I woke up when the nurse brought me the hospital version of baked chicken. I picked at it and ate the roll and butter. I just finished the last spoonful of vanilla pudding when Mike called.

"The kids want to see you. They were really upset when I told them you weren't coming home. I am going to bring them over for a little bit," Mike told me over the phone.

As much as I missed my kids, I did not want them to come. I didn't want them to see me like that but Mike insisted they would be alright. After the nurse took my tray, I hid my drains under my robe and covered up to my neck with an extra blanket. I straightened my knit cap and tried to look as normal as possible in a hospital bed.

I heard them coming down the hall. I recognized their footsteps and heard Kade reading the numbers on the doors. I saw Kalea first. She walked in tentatively, carrying a stuffed giraffe, looked at me with wide eyes and then at the ground. Kade was holding Mike's hand, and I could tell he was dragging Kade behind him. Kade, too, looked down at the ground, occasionally stealing a quick glance in my direction.

"Give Mommy her gifts, guys," Mike encouraged them. Kalea walked toward me with the giraffe. I reached my hand from under the blanket to accept it. Kalea quickly stepped back near Mike who gave Kade a nudge. He walked toward me with a small vase of flowers but I couldn't reach out with both hands to take the vase.

"Those are beautiful, Kade. You can give those to Daddy to put on my windowsill," Kade eagerly turned away from me to run back to Mike. The kids stood awkwardly for a few minutes until Mike told them to sit down in the chairs against the window.

"What have you been doing at home?" I asked them.

"Playing," said Kalea.

"Watching shows," said Kade.

They both looked around the room. Kalea read the dry erase board on the wall and turned to look out the window. Mike and I looked at each other, not sure what to say. The awkward silence was broken when the nurse entered the room.

"Hi there. I see you have visitors," she said, smiling at the kids. They didn't smile back.

"Can I ask you to step out for a moment so I can check on your mom?"

The nurse didn't wait long enough for them to leave before she turned down my blanket. I was afraid they saw the drains or my bloody bandages but thankfully, only my robe was visible.

"All done," the nurse yelled out in the hallway. "You can come back in to see your mommy," she told them. Mike pulled them both back into the room.

"It was great seeing you guys. Mommy will be home tomorrow," I said. "Maybe Daddy will take you for some ice cream on the way home."

Mike knew the kids were uncomfortable. I wanted to squeeze them and kiss their scared little faces but I couldn't. I would have to wait until tomorrow when I got home. Mike picked them up so they could kiss me goodbye.

"Love you guys," I said.

"Love you, Mommy," they both said as they waved and left. They couldn't get out of there fast enough.

Me too, guys. Me too.

Chapter Sixteen

Friends: I saw this and thought of you...
(Hands me a random item with a breast cancer ribbon on it.)

The first few days at home were awful. I could not stand up or sit down by myself. It hurt too much to sit upright for too long. Lying flat on my back was the only way to relieve tension and pain, but like a turtle, once on my back, I was stuck. I had to call for Mike to lift or lower me like a drawbridge. I was helpless. And I felt useless.

Several times a day I locked myself in the bathroom to empty my drains. I sat on the edge of the tub, removed the plastic bulb, and poured the fluid into a measuring cup. I recorded the amount of fluid in each drain and then dumped it in the toilet. When I finished measuring all the drains, I flushed the toilet. The whole process made me sick to my stomach.

"Ugh," I closed my eyes to keep from gagging. The worst part was rinsing that nasty measuring cup. I couldn't believe I had to do this until my first follow-up appointment a week after surgery. Dr. Patterson suggested at discharge that Mike help me with the drains. No way. I could do it by myself. I could use the bathroom on my own as well. That was a marriage barrier I wanted to keep in place.

Each day, the amount of bloody liquid decreased. Dr. Patterson could only remove the drains on my first office visit if the liquid decreased to a particular level. I couldn't wait to get them out of me. I hid them from the kids. They were so uncomfortable and I worried they would leak onto my clothes or onto the bed. As much as I wanted the drains gone, the thought of those tubes being pulled out of my body made me shudder.

I hid the measuring cup under the sink and clipped the drains to my robe. I went back to bed when Dr. Barton's office called.

"Hi Jennifer," said Caroline. "We got your report back. I wanted to go over it with you. Is this a good time?"

"Yes, I'm good."

"Ok," she started, "Of the six lymph nodes that were removed–".

"Mike said they told him five lymph nodes were removed," I interrupted.

"No," she said. "Sometimes, upon closer inspection, what they think is one might be two. The report shows six lymph nodes were removed and one of them tested positive for cancer. It was microscopic, but it was cancerous."

"What? Mike was told they were all clear. What does that mean?" I asked, starting to panic.

"Well, Dr. Barton wants to talk to you about it in more detail next week, but we feel it is best to plan for radiation. I know we said radiation wasn't necessary, but we need to put that back on the table." She paused for a moment, but I didn't know what to say.

"Let's talk next week and get you set up with a radiation oncologist."

A radiation oncologist? I had never heard of a radiation oncologist. Now, I had one of those too. I was devastated. I thought after my surgery, I was done with treatment. I could recover and go on with my life. Now, I had to go through radiation. More treatment, more time.

The following week, I sat around a large table with Dr. Barton and her team. The tumor was larger than they thought. Cancerous cells were found in all four sections of the left breast tissue. They did get clear margins. As a precaution, radiation to the chest wall was recommended.

The expanders inside my chest were made of metal. I couldn't have radiation with metal in my body. I had two options. I could have another surgery to remove the expanders, then radiation therapy followed by another surgery to place the expanders and start the reconstruction process again. Or, I could continue with the reconstruction process, at a faster pace, have the exchange surgery with the final implants and then begin radiation.

Not wanting to go through another surgery right away, I chose option two. I would discuss it with Dr. Patterson. It seemed I went two steps forward, five steps back. Hearing that my cancer was worse than they thought made me nervous. I was devastated I had to go through radiation. I thought I was done after reconstruction. Was this ever going to end?

God, everyone tells me that you don't give us more than we can handle. But I don't know how much more I can take. I did the chemo. I did the surgery. I will do the reconstruction. I hadn't planned on radiation. I keep holding on, pushing through but I don't know how much more I can do. Help me, Lord, to hold on to my faith, even when things don't make sense. Every time I think I am okay, something else knocks me down. I am trusting you, Lord. I don't like this. But I trust you that I will get through this too. Amen.

* *

Since Darcie cut back her hours, I checked in with her when I could. Often, I checked in with the staff member who answered the phone. Everyone assured me things were fine. I heard about squabbles here and there. The center suffered growing pains with increased enrollment and new staff. Overall, things seemed to be okay. I never got any bad reports.

As I worked on timesheets and payroll, I received an email notification. It was from one of my favorite clients. She had two boys at the center, an infant and a preschooler. The subject line was "concerned" and the email said, "I am sorry to bother you right now with all you are going through, but I thought you should see this."

I scrolled down to read the attachment. It was a forwarded email a staff member sent to all the parents. Jeannie, one of my trusted employees, sent a letter of resignation to all the parents that included a detailed account of the many reasons Jeannie decided to leave. Although her main reason was due to changes in her husband's work schedule, she cast an unfavorable light on the center. It was subtle, but it was there. Why would she do that? I just talked to her the other morning and everything was fine. How did she get the parent email list? I had so many questions.

I discussed it with Jeannie and Darcie in the morning. Jeannie apologized for the poor choice of words, but insisted she meant no harm. When I asked her why she didn't direct her resignation letter to me, she said Darcie told her not to bother me. They both thought the parents had a right to know she was leaving. I agreed, but sending parents a resignation letter was inappropriate. They both knew that. I asked Darcie why she gave Jeannie access to my client email list. She didn't think it was a big deal. I gave them the benefit of the doubt but I felt uneasy.

I sent an email to the parents to clear up any misunderstanding. I thanked the client who let me know what happened. The other parents were fine, but the incident added unnecessary stress I didn't need, or appreciate. I was recovering from the surgery, so I had little energy to waste. When the situation was resolved, I hoped we could move forward with no issues.

* *

Mom drove me to my appointment with Dr. Patterson. I wore an over-sized button down shirt and a big chunky cardigan to mask the drains I had pinned underneath. We sat in the beautifully decorated waiting room with solid wood furniture and plush chairs. Fresh flowers filled glass vases on the side tables. Classical music played in the background. A silver water pitcher and a plate of cookies sat on a table in the back of the room.

"This looks more like a spa than a doctor's office," I whispered in Mom's ear. This waiting room looked nothing like the ones at the hospital. Dr. Patterson put a lot of effort into creating a relaxing atmosphere. The room was beautiful, but I was preoccupied thinking about the drains being ripped from inside of me.

A professionally dressed woman in her 50's checked in and took a seat at the other side of the room. She had long, bleach blond hair and big blue, heavily lined eyes. Her lips were a perfect shade of red. She was beautiful. I couldn't help but wonder why she was there. Tummy tuck, face lift, boob job? She didn't need any of those things. She looked perfect.

A young nurse in blue scrubs, her hair pulled into a neat bun, approached me in the waiting room. "Jennifer?" she asked in a hushed tone. "You can follow me." Usually, the nurses screamed my name like I was waiting for a table at Texas Roadhouse. We walked through a long tiled hallway to a small room with hardwood cabinets and an upholstered chair. She placed a thick dusty rose gown on the exam table.

"Dr. Patterson will be in to see you in a few minutes," she whispered again. I changed and got on the exam table. A black and white historical photograph was displayed in a decorative wooden frame on the wall. I wondered if the people posed in front of a horse and buggy knew their portrait would hang on a doctor's wall one day, would they have smiled more? There was a knock at the door.

"Hi there. So, how are you feeling?" asked Dr. Patterson as she gently peeled off the bandages and inspected my incisions. I didn't look down.

"Healing nicely." She asked some questions and reviewed my drain measurement spreadsheet. "I think it is okay to remove the drains. That will make you feel more comfortable."

"Is it going to hurt?" I asked. Reading my anxiety, she assured me that it would not hurt.

"It might be uncomfortable. The nerve endings in that area are dead so you aren't going to feel pain. They come out so fast, you probably won't feel anything." I didn't believe her.

I closed my eyes as Dr. Patterson tugged on my side. I felt a weird sensation, as the plastic tubing slipped from the inside of my chest out the side of my body. She was right. It was fast. In less than a minute, the drains were gone. She bandaged the holes on my side and I was done. Nothing was sticking out of my body. No more measuring, dumping, or cleaning those gross drains.

Dr. Patterson scheduled my first 'fill' appointment in two weeks. She instructed me to get some additional rest and to eat extra protein. I was so happy when I met Mom in the waiting room.

"Drains are gone," I said, giving mom a thumbs up.

"Let's get out of here," Mom said. We left the office and mom drove me to the center.

Darcie wasn't there. Linda was in the infant room. She was a hard worker. She knew all the child care regulations. She was also a mom. Parents always felt more comfortable when a mom worked in the infant room. After Jeannie resigned, Linda stepped up. She worked well with the babies and young toddlers. I dropped off some supplies and walked into the office for the deposit Darcie left on the desk. It was the first time I had been in the office since our inspection a few months ago.

The office was a mess. Papers were stacked on both sides of the desk. Empty fast food cups were on the table near the couch. Boxes of art materials that never made it to the supply closet sat under the window. I threw away the cups and straightened the papers on the desk. I set up a frame with a picture of my kids on top of the bookshelf. It had been face down next to the monitor. If I were stronger, I would have done more. I took one last look at the office, waved to Linda on the way out, and left.

I couldn't wait to get back. My office needed a deep cleaning.

Chapter Seventeen

"Even the darkest night will end and the sun will rise."
VICTOR HUGO

My first 'fill' was coming up. I called Christi one evening so we could discuss the reconstruction process. She was such a wonderful source of information and she became a good friend.

"It's not too bad. I used to get my fills and then go shopping," Christi said. "This part was pretty easy for me. My doctor did a really good job."

"Dr. Patterson told me I could take Ibuprofen. She said some women don't have a problem, but some are sore for a couple of days."

"I think you will be fine," she said. "Good luck. Let me know how it goes."

I told Mom what Christi said as we sat in Dr. Patterson's waiting room. We planned to go to lunch after my appointment. We hadn't gone since my surgery. Doing things I used to do made me feel normal again. I looked forward to it. I couldn't drive myself so I enjoyed getting out of the house.

"Let's see how you feel when you are done," Mom said. "If you don't feel up to it, we can have lunch another time."

"I'll be fine," I insisted. The nurse whispered my name and took me to a room with a different old photo on the wall; this one of a family standing on a porch of an old farmhouse.

We discussed the plan for my reconstruction and radiation. Because I needed to start radiation as soon as possible, I would have the fill appointments more frequently than usual. The expanders would be exchanged for regular implants. It was not optimal to have radiation with implants but it was the best solution outside of removing the expanders.

Dr. Patterson prepared a syringe and inserted the needle to access the first expander. I felt pressure but no pain as the needle broke the skin. Then, I watched as the temporary implant grew a little larger. I felt some tightening in my chest, but it did not hurt. She repeated the process on the other side. Again, pressure, but no pain. When I lifted my arms to put on my winter coat, it felt like my chest was wrapped in tight bandages.

"Okay," she said. "Go home and rest. You might be sore later today or for the next couple of days. Did you pick up the pain meds I called in for you?"

"Yes," I said. "Those were some strong pain meds. Do you think I will need them?"

"See how you feel. Some women don't have any pain. Some find it very uncomfortable."

"Okay," I said. "So I will see you in a couple of weeks?"

"Yes. Call if you need anything," she said as she walked out the door.

I talked Mom into stopping for lunch. I felt fine when we left the office, but by the time our food was served I started to feel uncomfortable. We ate quickly. Slowly the pressure turned to pain. It hurt to breathe. On the ride home, every bump in the road made me cry out in agony. When we finally pulled into the driveway, I got out of the car and into the house. Mike heard us come in.

"What's wrong?" he asked and rushed to my side.

I couldn't speak because it hurt too much to form words. I pointed up the stairs. Mike held onto my waist as he walked me to the bedroom. He helped me sit on the chair, but the pressure didn't stop. Tears streamed down my face but I couldn't cry. It would hurt.

"I...need...to lie...down," I said in short spurts through the pain. He helped me up and across the room to the bed. I took the pain pill and muscle relaxer Dr. Patterson prescribed "just in case". I hated pain meds, but I needed them. Only when I was completely flat did I find the tiniest bit of relief. I held my breath for long periods of time, afraid to inhale deeply and engage the muscles in my chest and back. For hours, I stared at the ceiling, and fought through the pain. Long after the sun had set, the room lit by the nightstand lamp, I was able to take a full breath without excruciating pain. My whole body ached from enduring the pain. Finally, in the late evening, once I could breathe normally, I was able to get out of bed and go downstairs.

Mike was surprised when I walked into the family room.

"How are you?" he asked standing up to help me sit on the couch.

"That was awful. I couldn't breathe. That medicine didn't touch the pain."

"You have to do that every two weeks?"

I nodded.

I couldn't say that out loud. I didn't want to think about doing that again.

* *

"Look at these!" I said to Mom, holding up two stuffed monkeys with hearts on them. They were the perfect addition to the Valentine's Day baskets for the kids. It had been a few days since my first fill and I was feeling better. Mom and I went for lunch and stopped at the store to browse the Valentine's Day decorations and gifts.

"I will make heart shaped cookies for Wednesday," I told Mom, picking up some pink sprinkles.

"Why on Wednesday?", Mom asked.

"For Valentine's Day!" I said.

"Valentine's Day isn't on Wednesday. It's on Thursday!". My shoulders dropped as I counted the days on my fingers.

"No! My appointment is on Thursday!"

I wanted to cry.My next fill appointment with Dr Patterson was on Valentine's Day. We always had chocolate fondue with the kids. I'd be upstairs trying not to breathe. Maybe it would be okay. Like my shot, maybe it was only bad the first time.

I never really cared for Valentine's Day. I thought it was silly. We never celebrated like other couples. We exchanged cards, maybe some candy. We didn't go to dinner either. We didn't like the crowds.

My dad passed away on February 13th. He had been in the hospital and come home the day before. I spent most of those last 2 weeks at the hospital with him and at my parents' house on the day he came home. That evening, once he was settled, I left to go back home. I hadn't seen Mike much and I was exhausted. I took a break the next day to do things around the house and get some work done. My mom went back to work but my aunt stayed with my dad. I planned to go back to visit the following day.

That night, Mom called to say Dad passed out in the bathroom and she called an ambulance. I packed a bag and left to meet Mom at the hospital. It was about an hour drive. I wondered if Dad's medicine was wrong again. I thought they sent him home too soon. Maybe a couple more days would be good for him. He was not going to be happy. He hated the hospital.

It was after midnight when I arrived. I parked in the emergency lot and walked through the sliding doors like I had dozens of times. I approached the nurse's desk and gave the short, dark haired nurse my father's name. She hesitated for a moment then came around the front of the desk.

"Follow me," she said and turned left. I knew the rooms were to the right. I followed her around the corner to a long hallway until she stopped at a door, motioning for me to go inside.

"Your mom is in there," she said. I looked at her, confused. She turned and walked away.

The sign on the door said, "Family". I turned the knob and opened the door. My mom sat on a couch next to a hospital employee. She was crying. She looked up and shook her head. That's when I knew. Dad was gone.

A day later, Mike arrived at my parent's house carrying two bouquets of roses. One for me and one for my mom. It was Valentine's Day. I never liked Valentine's Day, but now I hated it.

We didn't celebrate Valentine's Day again until the kids were old enough to celebrate with us. We started a new tradition including little gifts for the kids and chocolate fondue. After my surgery and the first fill appointment, I was really looking forward to a fun celebration. Now, it probably wouldn't happen.

"It will be okay," Mike insisted later at dinner. "Maybe it won't be that bad. If it is, we can celebrate another day."

I did not want to celebrate on another day. I wanted to celebrate on Valentine's Day.

Stupid cancer.

* *

I walked to the car as fast as I could. The tightness began immediately this time. So did the pain. It was going to get worse. I told Mom to get me home as quickly as she could. Every stop and acceleration, every bump and turn was excruciating. Mike heard us pull in and met me at the door. He walked me upstairs and got me onto the bed.

I stayed there for hours, manipulating my breath to minimize the pain. It didn't work, but forced my mind to focus on something else. When the kids got home from school, Mike opened the door to tell me the kids had gifts and cards for me. I couldn't make it downstairs yet and I didn't want them to see me in so much pain.

"I'll tell them we can do it after dinner. We can have the fondue and then you can go back to bed," Mike planned. He didn't know how badly this hurt or how debilitating it was.

I hoped I would be okay by dinnertime. I wasn't. I didn't want to disappoint the kids so Mike helped me downstairs on the couch, propping me up with pillows. I was in so much pain, but wanted to be with my family on Valentine's Day.

"Mommy, look what I made for you," said Kalea, holding a hand-made card.

"That's...beautiful," I managed, still only able to speak a word at a time. Every word caused those muscles to move and pain shot through my entire body. Kalea moved toward me for a hug.

"Easy," said Mike. "Mommy still hurts." She stopped short, her face falling. It broke my heart. I reached out to rub her back, the pain taking my breath.

"Thank you, Sweet Pea," I said, as naturally as I could. "Love you."

"Love you, Mommy!", Kalea said as she jumped up on the couch beside me. Her weight shifted the pillows around me. I looked away so she didn't see my tears.

Kade brought his card over next. Witnessing the interaction with Kalea, he stood a few feet away and stretched his arm out to hand me the card. He didn't want to hurt me.

"I love it, Bud," I said. "Come here."He walked toward me and I reached out my arms and pulled him closer. He leaned in and I hugged him the best I could. "Love you, Little Man"

"Love you, Mommy," he said and walked away to play with his cars. Mike looked at me from across the room.

"You want me to take you back upstairs?" Mike asked. I wasn't fooling him. With all of my heart, I wanted to stay there but I couldn't. The pain was too intense and I didn't want to scare the kids. I nodded and the disappointed tears fell. Mike helped me off the couch and back upstairs to bed.

"We will celebrate big time next year," he whispered, trying to make me feel better.

As evening fell, it grew dark. The small lamp lit the room, casting shadows on the walls. It was quiet. I heard Mike and the kids downstairs, enjoying Valentine's Day fondue without me. I felt so alone. Isolated. Tired of all of it.

"You got more chocolate on your hands than you did in your mouth," Mike teased.

"Daddy, can we have more rice crispy treats?" asked Kade.

"Strawberries are my favorite," Kalea chimed in.

Their squeals and giggles carried from downstairs. I couldn't help but smile, and then tears fell down the sides of my face. I couldn't lift my arms to wipe them so I let them soak into my pillow. I was in pain. I was alone and angry, stuck in those feelings like I was stuck in that bed. I would have screamed, but it would hurt too much.

I thought about my dad in those last years. He was in pain all the time. On top of his renal disease and heart problems, he suffered from terrible neuropathy in his feet. The meds that helped his disease caused nerve damage and muscle aches.

"It feels like someone is stabbing me with ice picks, over and over again. It never stops," he used to say. His doctors prescribed medication but nothing helped. "Sometimes, I sit up at night when the pain is so bad, tears rolling down my face. I just want some relief, but it never comes."

It hurt my heart when he told me that, but I didn't understand. I had no idea what that felt like. Now I did. I wasn't sure what I could have said or what I could have done back then, but I wished it was more. I now understood the pain and isolation he felt.

"It doesn't do any good to complain," he told me. "It doesn't make you feel any better. It just makes you think about it more. Just have to keep going."

"I'm trying, Dad," I whispered.

Chapter Eighteen

"You may shoot me with your words,
You may cut me with your eyes,
You may kill me with your hatefulness,
But still, like life I'll rise."

MAYA ANGELOU

I was really tired. I put the kids to bed and forced myself to do some work. I had to do as much as I could before my next fill. I moved my laptop to the kitchen counter and put a pillow on the barstool to make it more comfortable. I answered a couple emails from parents and my accountant. I finished some bookkeeping when an email from Linda, the infant teacher, appeared in my inbox, the subject, "Resignation".

"What?" I said out loud and opened the email.

My heart sank. Linda was quitting, but she didn't just give her two weeks notice. She wrote terrible things about me and the center. I couldn't believe it. She said everyone felt the same. The staff thought I was selfish and only thought about money. I suffered from "chemo brain" and made poor business decisions. I didn't value them or the hard work they did. The parents thought I didn't care about my employees or their children. Her words pierced my heart. Nothing she said was true, nor did it make any sense. I was reading it again when Mike walked into the kitchen.

"What's wrong?" he asked. I pointed to the screen and moved so he could sit down.

"What is this?" he asked. "This is ridiculous. If I ever wrote a

135

letter like that to my boss, I would be fired. And I would never send something like that to anyone." Mike paced the kitchen.

Speechless, I tried to understand why someone I considered a friend would say such horrible things. Mike leaned back against the kitchen counter, arms across his chest.

"I'm going over there tomorrow. If they are all unhappy, they can find another job," he said.

"No, I can't do that to the kids and their families. Their parents need to work. Those kids need a place to go. It isn't their fault."

It all made sense now. I had been getting odd emails and phone calls from parents. Their concerns were easily answered. I thought they were just nervous since I had been away from the center. I brushed it off.

The more the pieces came together, the more devastated I became. I thought the staff was stressed because our enrollment increased so quickly. I thought that was why they seemed standoffish and quiet. I couldn't wait to get back to work to help and to alleviate some of their stress. The other day, Mike and I talked about throwing a party to thank them for all they did. And money? I hadn't taken a paycheck or made a profit since my diagnosis. I considered some of the parents my friends. I considered my staff as family. What Linda wrote in that email? None of it could have been further from the truth.

"I can't just stand here and do nothing," Mike said. "I can't let this go. They have no right to treat you that way. With all you are going through, you don't need this," he ranted.

"I know," I said. "That's the thing. With all I am going through, I can't deal with this."

I wasn't strong enough. I was fighting for my life. I didn't have the physical or mental energy to fight against these women. I was devastated. Embarrassed. I wanted to defend myself. Tell the staff and the parents that none of this was true. I didn't deserve this.

My words had been misunderstood. Rules had to be followed, whether I was in the building or not. Working with children was hard. Working with parents was hard. I made decisions that were the best for the center. As all the conversations and happenings over the last few months swirled in my head, I understood. People I trusted had twisted my words. They blamed me. They carried tales. They threw me under the bus. It was so deep, so far gone, there wasn't much I could do. I couldn't fire everyone. I couldn't close the center. I wasn't physically able to go back to work. I couldn't defend myself against words and unfair assumptions. I had to give it to God and not take it back. I was used to figuring things out on my own, but this time I couldn't.

I didn't want people to think badly of me, but I had to let my character speak for itself. Those who knew me, knew better. I couldn't control what people thought, only how I lived my life. Linda's words were not a reflection of who I was.

Over the next couple of weeks, Darcie and Mary quit too. A few loyal employees stayed to help me. They worked crazy shifts until I hired new staff and things calmed down. I took a few phone calls from concerned parents. It was easy to tell which parents believed what they heard.

When a parent invited me to lunch, I was excited to receive the invitation. It would be nice to see a friendly face and to get out of the house. We chose a restaurant nearby so Mom could drive me. I felt like a child unable to drive myself, but I was happy to be going anywhere other than a doctor appointment.

Leslie and I greeted and hugged each other, then the waitress showed us to our table. After I filled her in on what was going on with treatment, she asked how everything else was going. I assumed she meant the center.

"It's been hard. I was surprised by the resignations and a little embarrassed about what people thought about me –"

"Alright," Leslie interrupted. "Since I am friends with some of them, I really don't want to talk about any of that. There are two sides to every story."

The waitress brought our food but I was no longer hungry. Her loyalty was clearly with the others. I never planned to talk badly about them. I only wanted to tell her my side and how it hurt me. I thought she was my friend.

"Okay," I stammered. I moved my food around on the plate, trying not to cry.

Leslie broke the silence by talking about her work and her family. It was awkward. We finished eating and settled the bill. We hugged and said goodbye. I left wondering why she invited me. Mom picked me up at the door.

"How was lunch?" Mom asked.

"She's with them," I said.

After a few more fill appointments, it was time for my exchange surgery. My expanders would be removed and breast implants would be placed under those stretched muscles. It was such a relief that I wouldn't have to go through another fill. Those long hours in pain were wearing on me on top of the stress of the center.

"Some women go through the process with only mild discomfort," said Dr. Patterson. "For others, it is a very painful process. I am sorry that you were one of the latter, but we are done. No more fills. We will schedule your exchange surgery and you can put this part behind you."

"Finally," I told Mike on the way to the hospital, "I am finally going to be done with this part. Then, I can start radiation. I just want to be done with all of it!".

"I know," he said. "Almost there!"

We arrived at the hospital and registered. I wasn't nervous this time. Surgery was no fun, but this recovery would be much easier. We would be home by lunch. By this time, Mike and I knew the drill. I changed into my gown and socks. After they inserted the IV, they let Mike hang out with me until they were ready. I said goodbye to Mike and then they wheeled me to the pre-op room with all the other patients.

I woke up in the recovery room. My eyes were closed but I heard the voices and the buzz around me. I knew it was over.

"How are you feeling?" a nurse asked a nearby patient.

"She's going back upstairs," said another nurse from across the room. I heard people talking and machines beeping all at once. The room was full of activity. As hard as I tried, my eyes wouldn't open.

"Hey, there," I heard someone say and I felt a hand gently patting my arm. "You waking up?" I had to concentrate to make my eyelids open. I tried, but it didn't work.

"I'll give you a few minutes," the nurse said and walked away.

I eventually opened my eyes. Everything was fuzzy.An older man with his leg in a cast sat in the bed across from me. I glanced at my chest to make sure I was covered. The patient beds formed a circle. I saw men and women, young and old, in different stages of conscious-

THE IN-BETWEEN IS EVERYTHING

ness. I had to sign all those privacy forms, but there really was no privacy in a hospital.

Over the next week or so, I changed my bandages as instructed. I noticed one side seeped more than the other. It happened to be the cancer side.

My friend Melissa invited me to a Dave Matthews Band concert. I was feeling good and agreed to go. I went to my first DMB concert with my friend Heidi. We took back roads to avoid traffic on the way home and got lost until three in the morning. We both had to get up for work the next morning, but it was totally worth it. We had such a fun night. The music also reminded me of the summer I met Mike. I was so happy to be out and living again. During the concert, I felt warmth in the bandages. I figured my incision seeped more because I was moving more. The next day, it continued so I called Dr. Patterson. She wanted to see me right away.

I arrived the next morning and the nurse gently removed the bandages. She looked away for a moment, then forced a smile while she applied a fresh bandage. "Dr. Patterson will be in to see you in just a few minutes." I knew something was wrong.

Dr. Patterson walked in with a concerned look on her face.

"Sometimes, when you have chemotherapy, it affects your ability to heal. Your incision is not healing. It is open and your implant is visible. As a cancer patient, you have an increased risk of infection. The implant needs to come out. I can do that here in the office. I will puncture the implant. There will be a lot of fluid. I can remove it. We will put you on antibiotics and then schedule another surgery to replace the implant."

"You mean it has to come out? I have to do this all over again?" I asked, unable to hold back the tears. Dr. Patterson put her hand on my shoulder.

"Yes, but if you are more comfortable going to the hospital, we can do it there. It is up to you." I didn't want to go to the hospital.

"Just do it," I said.

She draped a gown and a few towels over my lap. I felt no pain. I heard the liquid splashing on the floor and then some pressure as the implant was removed. All that hope I felt the night before spilled out on the floor. Another setback. She closed the incision with tape and wrapped my chest in gauze and bandages. I was flat on one side. Dr. Patterson gave me a cotton insert to place inside my bra.

Mom drove me home but Mike and I had to go straight to the school for Kalea's portfolio day. I wouldn't miss it. Another defeat, but like Dad always said, "No sense in complaining."

"Mommy, over here!" Kalea yelled, pointing to the seat beside her. She was so excited to see us. We looked through her schoolwork and chose special items to place in her 'time capsule' portfolio.

"I get to write a letter to you. It will stay in your portfolio until you open it in a few years. You will get it back when you leave elementary school," I told Kalea. She talked to her friends while I wrote the letter. I took my time. I wrote about all the fun times during the school year and how proud I was of her. I never passed up the opportunity to tell her how much I loved her.

* *

Things were finally settling down at the center. Jenn was young but great with the kids and the parents. She was a hard worker too. Charlie lived nearby. She was a strong Christian woman and did a great job in the classroom and the office. Charlie asked to meet for coffee and tea. After lunch with Leslie, I hesitated but accepted.

We met at a coffee shop and I filled her in on the reconstruction process and upcoming radiation. She gave me a prayer shawl she had her church friends knit for me. It was lovely. I had been feeling pretty lonely and isolated. I was stuck in the house. I couldn't drive. I was in pain most of the time. After everything that happened, I wasn't sure who I could trust anymore. When Charlie gave me such a meaningful gift, it touched my heart. We caught up on our families and then inevitably, the conversation moved to the center.

Some members of the staff had been unhappy for a long time. My absence allowed grievances to fester. Those left in charge didn't feel comfortable supervising others. Instead of enforcing rules, those rules were blamed on me. Instead of explaining the reasoning behind the rules, the staff was told I was unable to make sound decisions, that what I was asking was unfair and unreasonable. The staff grew angry with me. Everything fell apart.

I stopped by to drop off checks or supplies often. When I said goodbye and closed the door, staff would sometimes make fun of me. One day, they made fun of my wig.

"I was shocked and ashamed," Charlie said. "You were fighting for your life, and that was how they carried on? Disgraceful."She didn't tell me much more. I didn't want to hear it.

"That hurts," I said, taking in what she just told me, "But I gave it all to God. I don't have any control over what people say or think about me. I can't worry about others' opinions anymore. I couldn't let that define me."

Later I told Mike what I learned. He was angry enough for the both of us. I wasn't angry anymore. Broken maybe, but not angry. Things worked out at the center. I didn't have to do anything. God took care of it. I let it go. I held my head high. I didn't do anything wrong.

They couldn't do the same.

Chapter Nineteen

"You know, your haircut still looks like a boy's haircut, but you aren't scary looking anymore. The skin on your head has hair on it now and it doesn't look like the same skin that is on your face. You could even walk around the house looking like that, Mom"

KADE, AGE 6

My hair was short and curly. I didn't like it but was grateful to have it. I pulled my hair products from under the cabinet where I hid them months ago. I trimmed my nails removing the last of the deep ridges caused by chemo and painted my now healthy nails a pretty shade of pink. My hands looked familiar to me again. With each new day, I felt more whole on the outside.

I was a naturally positive person. I wore a smile on my face and went through my day, but there were those times when I felt completely alone. That was when I cried out to God and drew closest to Him. I talked to God like He was sitting in the room with me. Sometimes, I spoke out loud. I confessed my guilt for putting the wrong things first. I failed to see the blessings in my life. I thought I had it all together. I was married to a wonderful husband and had two beautiful kids. I owned two businesses I worked so hard to build. I had a warm house, nice clothes, and a reliable car. I checked all the boxes. I was living the life. Turned out, I wasn't living at all.

Cancer entered my life and opened my eyes. God didn't give me cancer, but God used cancer to change my life. He was working on me—knitting me back together, stronger than before. I was a work in progress. There was still more left to do, but I was more gentle, more patient, more loving. My senses were heightened. I noticed the sunset, the sound of my kid's laughter. Chocolate chip cookies were more delicious.

I'm all in, God. Take my heart. Take my soul. Take all of me until there is nothing left. Make me a better person. Use me for your purpose. I am yours, Lord. Give me the strength to keep going. I will praise your name for the rest of my life.

* *

"We need to go to the mall and get you two some spring clothes," I announced to the kids. It was such a beautiful day after a week of gloomy weather. The forecast called for high 70's later in the week. The kids grew out of their shorts from last summer. A trip to the mall sounded like fun.

"Can we stop at the candy store?" asked Kade. He was not a fan of shopping for clothes.

"If you guys are good while we are shopping, then yes!"

I helped the kids find their shoes and put them on, reminding Kade to put them on the right feet. I picked up my purse and my keys and walked toward the door.

"Oh, I have to run upstairs and get my wig," I said. I almost forgot I wasn't wearing it. I had grown so used to walking around the house with my short hair.

"Why?" Kade asked.

"Why do you have to wear your wig? Why can't you go like that?" Kalea asked.

"You look pretty like that, Mommy," said Kade pointing to my hair.

The pleading looks on their faces caught me off guard.

"Can you please go like that, mommy?" Kalea asked.

"Okay," I said. "Let's go." I was uneasy as we walked out the door.

As they buckled themselves into their booster seats, I felt the spring breeze on my ears and my neck. I looked in the rearview mirror. My hair was so short and not me.

"I'm so happy you aren't wearing your wig, mommy," Kade said a few minutes later.

We found cute spring clothes for both of them. Shorts and tops and even sandals. As promised, we stopped at the candy store on the way out.

"Grab a bag. I will scoop," I said as they stared at the cases of candy on the wall. Kade chose gummy sharks and sour soda bottles. Kalea got sour cherries and strawberry belts.

"I will give them to you in the car," I said after we checked out. Kade asked to carry the bag.

"Thank you both for being so good," I said, handing Kade the bag. They skipped ahead of me, anxious to eat their candy.

I saw my reflection in a window. I survived my first trip in public with my super short hair. The kids were quiet on the way home. I turned on the radio and rolled down the window to feel the breeze blow on my face and through my hair. When we got home, the kids asked to play outside. I sat on the front stoop while the kids played ball in the yard. The evening sun was shining through the tree in the front yard and the golden rays warmed my face.

"Watch, Mom," they said with every kick of the ball.

They were so happy. It had been a long winter. The fresh air and spring weather was good for all of us. I noticed the hostas were sprouting in the mulch and a few dandelions popped up in the yard.

While the kids played, I thought about my hair. It would be forever before I had bangs or until I could pull it up in a ponytail. A breeze blew up the back of my neck as afternoon turned to evening. I shivered. After all I had been through, I should have been grateful to sit outside with my kids on a beautiful spring day, not feeling sorry for myself.

My neighbor Dan pulled into his driveway and waved. A moment later, he walked across the street. I didn't have time to get my wig.

"Hi there," he said, taking a seat next to me on the porch. "How are you?"

We made small talk for a few minutes. I asked how Erin and the kids were doing and rambled about how the kids didn't want me to wear my wig to the mall.

"I think your hair looks nice," he said, nothing insincere in his tone. People said a lot of obligatory things to you when you were sick.

"Thank you," I said. I was embarrassed but a kind word was what I needed to hear. We talked a little while longer before he got up to leave.

"Take care. Have a nice night," I said as Dan waved goodbye.

The sun popped out from behind the clouds and I had to squint my eyes to see.

"Ok, God, I know," I said out loud. "I shouldn't have been so worried about my hair, but enjoyed this spring day with my kids."

"Who are you talking to, Mom?" asked Kalea.

"God," I answered.

"Oh," she said. "Okay." She went back to playing with the ball.

Chapter Twenty

*"Oh, Jen, I am so sorry. If there is anything I can do for you,
ANYTHING, please let me know. You can call me any time, day
or night," said an insincere acquaintance at an abnormal-
ly loud volume in front of a group of women, in order to call
attention to herself as a nice person.
Later that night, I couldn't decide if I should call her and tell
her I had a hankering for a pint of ice cream, or a bucket of
fried chicken...*

It took a few weeks, but my incision finally healed. Dr. Patterson
scheduled the surgery to replace the implant she removed. Mike and I
arrived at the hospital that morning, hopefully for the last time. When
Dr. Patterson came in the recovery, she told me things went well, but
there were some complications.

"This implant is smaller than the other one and will 'hold the
place' since your muscle has been stretched through reconstruction.
You worked hard for those muscles. We don't want to go backwards
and lose that. I placed it a little higher to keep it out of the way during
radiation. Typically radiation was done before implants. Once you are
finished with radiation and healed properly, we can exchange that implant for one of the right size and reposition it."

I wasn't concerned about it. I was done with surgery. That was all
that mattered.

* *

"Extra butter, please," I said. "Can you layer it?" The teenage boy at the concession stand let out a bothered sigh, but nothing was going to ruin my mood. It was July 3, 2013. Opening day for *Despicable Me 2*.

"Can we get candy, Mommy?" Kade asked. We didn't have time to stop at the dollar store like we usually did.

"Sure, Bud! Today is a celebration. What do you want?"

"Can I get an Icee instead of candy, Mommy?" Kalea asked. "Please?"

"Yes, cherry or blue raspberry?"

"Blue!" she said.

After we loaded up on snacks, we walked into the theater and took our seats. The theater was crowded, but four seats were open in the back row. The lights dimmed and the movie started. I made it. As the minions came on the big screen, the kids giggled and bounced in their seats. I thought I might cry through the movie, emotions getting the best of me. No more tears. I grabbed a handful of popcorn and sat back in my seat. I was here. I enjoyed the show.

* *

"My grandfather had radiation. He had terrible burns. He was in so much pain. His skin looked charred. It was really gross" said a mom in the pickup line.

"You have to do radiation?" said a fellow cancer patient in the waiting room, "I had to do that. It was awful. Burned me so bad. I got infections from the burns and it put me in the hospital for a week."

"Radiation was worse than chemo for me. I had so many problems. I haven't been the same since. My skin looks awful. Your skin will cook and be tough and leathery forever," said another patient.

It was amazing how eager people were to tell me terrible things. Cancer and treatments were different for everyone. No one's story was the same. What did people get out of telling me these things? I would never do that to anyone. Ever.

Mike went with me to my first appointment with Dr. Kalani. His office was in a new building decorated in a modern style and calm colors. No beige and not one porch print. I didn't wait long before a nurse named Colleen called me to the exam room. She reviewed my information and checked my vitals.

"I'm going to get you a shirt," she said as she left the room. I assumed she meant a gown. I wasn't expecting a full exam today, just a consultation with the doctor.

"Here you go," she said, "This is your dignity shirt." It was a simple t-shaped shirt velcroed together down the front and along the seam of each arm allowing for access during radiation. The shirt was white with tiny multi-colored bunches of colorful pastel balloons all over it, trimmed in very dark green lace. It was the most festive and most awful shirt I had ever seen. I loved it.

"Oh my, this is something, isn't it?" I asked Colleen, smiling. She told me these shirts were lovingly sewn by volunteers. I was sure they were wonderful, but the shirt was a sight to see.

"Yes, it is," she said laughing. "I'm going to get your husband. Dr. Kalani will be in to see you soon."

Mike sat in the chair next to me. We were both nervous. Dr. Kalani immediately put us at ease with his big smile and warm demeanor.

"We are prescribing radiation treatment as a precaution. When we see cancer in the lymph nodes, there is concern a rogue cancer cell may have entered the chest wall. Radiation can minimize the odds of recurrence."

I would never refuse recommended treatment, even with all the scary things people told me. I would do anything to decrease a chance of recurrence.

"I'm sorry, but I have to tell you all the bad stuff that might happen. Most of my patients do very well. Radiation has come a long way in just the last few years. We can pinpoint the areas much better with less damage to the surrounding area." He explained the risks and what I could expect.

"So, after hearing all of that," he continued, "Do you want to go through with radiation?"

"Yes, I mean, I don't want to," I said. "But I want to do everything I can do now. I don't want to do this again."

Mike didn't speak, but shook his head in agreement.

"You will have to come back for a simulation, similar to a CT or

MRI scan. I am sure you are familiar with those by now. We will get you set up, take pictures, and tattoo little dots on your chest to set up the machines properly," explained Dr. Kalani.

"I don't want tattoos," I said. My friend Tammi already warned me about the tattoos and told me I could refuse. I didn't want radiation tattoos for the rest of my life.

"Okay," Dr. Kalani said, a little frustrated but still smiling. "Then we will mark you with a permanent marker and cover it with tape. It is not my preference to do it that way, but we can if that is the way you want to go."

"I do," I said, standing my ground.

"After the simulation, we will start radiation. I am prescribing 28 rounds of radiation. Sometimes it is 35 but I think we can do it in 28. I am going to let you off easy, see?" he said smiling.

"I like easy," I said. "I would appreciate it if something was easy."

"I'll see you next time. Very nice to meet you both."

"We are going to take very good care of her," Dr. Kalani said to Mike, sensing how nervous Mike was.

Colleen set up my appointment and gave me a packet of information.

"You are going to be okay! Bring your balloon shirt," reminded Colleen. "We will see you next week."

We both walked out feeling better about radiation and we both loved Dr. Kalani.

"Twenty-eight treatments. About six weeks," I said. "I can do this!".

"I know you can," Mike said as he grabbed my hand. "Almost there."

* *

I didn't want to go back to my old ways, but I had so much to do; so much to catch up on. I had to be careful. I couldn't work too many hours. If I did too much, I paid for it. During a follow-up appointment with Dr. Mendez, I couldn't hide how tired I was.

"Jen, I want you to do me a favor," said Dr. Mendez. "I know you want to get out there and do all the things you used to do. I know that you want to live like you aren't sick–"

"Yes?" I interrupted.

"But you need to remember that you are still a cancer patient, even just every once in a while." I knew what he meant. I wanted my life back, but I had to be more patient with myself.

"I know," I said. "I am feeling better, though."

"You think you are feeling better because you aren't on chemo anymore. Those meds are still in your body. You are going to feel better as time goes on. Your body took a hit. Your body needs rest and time to heal."

He was right. When I pushed too hard, my body revolted and it took a long time to recover. I promised not to go back to the way things were. I didn't know it was going to be so hard.

I called my friend Heidi on the way home from my appointment. She was like me. We both put too much pressure on ourselves to do things perfectly. Maybe that was why we got along so well.

When she answered the phone, I knew something was wrong. I heard it in her voice.

"I just got off the phone. Debbie isn't doing well," she said.

"What's going on?" I asked. I hadn't heard from Debbie in a while. The last we spoke, she was feeling a little better. She made a bucket-list of things she wanted to do. The new trial was working but that was no longer the case. Her body wasn't handling the treatment well. She promised to keep me updated. I sent Debbie a message to let her know I was praying for her. My message went unanswered. A few days later, Heidi called to tell me Debbie passed away.

"No!" I said, my heart breaking. She was doing better.

I cried myself to sleep that night. Debbie's green light was always on during those long nights when I was up with worry or in pain. We talked about things I couldn't talk about with our families. We kept each other going. We hated cancer and we weren't going to let it take anymore than it already had. But cancer took Debbie.

Debbie left this earth before she could put a checkmark next to any of those things on her bucket-list. My bucket list changed when I got cancer. My old bucket-list consisted of things related to my career. I made bucket-lists for summer and for Christmas break with the kids. Now, lists were too much pressure. The quest to complete the list became more important than enjoying the activities. I didn't want my life to be a checklist anymore. My life was a blank sheet of paper ready to be filled with great experiences. Life happened all around me, every day. There were highlights, of course, but those 'in between' times were the best times.

My "in-between" was spending time with my family and friends, not skydiving. I wanted to bake, read, cook, and write. Arrange pretty flowers in a vase. Drink hot tea. Sit by the window. Make pancakes on Saturday mornings. More lunch dates with my mom and date nights with Mike. Afternoons at the park with my kids. I didn't want to be too busy to notice the sunsets and the fall leaves, the blue sky and puffy-white-clouds, or the sound of birds singing and rain falling. I chased the wrong things my whole life. Other people could make their bucket-lists, but I didn't have one anymore.

Chapter Twenty-One

Walking to the car from the grocery store, tired and not feeling well after a chemo treatment, I saw an old woman struggling to load her bags into the car. She looked around, not knowing what to do. A man walked toward her. Relieved, she smiled at him and stepped away from the cart so he could get to them.
He walked past her and got in the car parked beside her.
"Do you need some help?" I asked...

Mommy, this song reminds me of you!" Kalea said, jumping onto the couch next to me, knocking my book onto the floor.

"What song is that?" I asked, reaching for my book.

"This song," she announced, then fumbled with her kindle.

A few moments later, I heard the beginning of Rachel Platten's *Fight Song*.

"Why does this remind you of me?"

"Because you fight cancer, Mommy. That's why. This can be your fight song."

I hugged her and pulled her close. She rested her head on my chest, smiled, and looked up at me as I listened. I didn't know how the kids processed everything. We tried to be honest without giving them more information than necessary. I wondered if they fully understood. I wiped the tears as I listened to the rest of the song. She knew more than I thought she did. I hoped one day my kids would know how hard I fought for them.

* *

Heidi called me on her way home from work. She was a busy woman, but checked in with texts and phone calls. She asked how I was doing. She complained about work and gushed about her girls. She asked for my advice and vented about the hard things going on in her life. She made me feel normal. Some people only wanted to talk about me. When I asked how they were, they said, "I don't want to complain to you" or "Nothing like anything you are dealing with". I wanted to hear what was going on with them. I wanted them to complain about their boss or their mother-in-law. I wanted to know about their health problems. My cancer didn't outweigh other people's problems. There was no rating scale. Everyone had something. Having cancer didn't make me incapable of being their friend. Heidi never made me feel that way.

* *

I changed into a gown and walked into the room. When Dr. Kalani said the simulation was like having an MRI, I didn't think it would be exactly like an MRI. I heard the clangs and screeches inside the machine and those awful noises brought back memories I buried deep. I didn't know if I could make it through the test. I prayed for God to help me.

Please Lord, I am scared. I didn't know this machine would make me feel so weak and so vulnerable. I didn't know this machine would take me right back to those early days when my world was crashing down. It is taking all I have not to crawl out of this machine and run out of this room, in this awful gown if need be. Please. I need your strength and your peace. Silence the noise, slow my heart, and ease my soul.

"I felt like a patient again," I told Susan over lunch the next day, trying not to cry. "I was right back to when I was first diagnosed. It wasn't the machines. It was the feelings. I thought I was over it, but that is still in me. I don't want to have radiation. I don't know if I can do it."

"You got through chemo. You got through surgery, that terrible reconstruction process," Susan encouraged me. "You have 28 treatments. You can do this!"

She was right. I had been through so much already. God got me this far, He would get me through these 28 treatments.

After dinner, I told the kids about my radiation treatment. I was honest with them. They were 6 and 7 and had already been through so much, but I wanted them to know what was going on.

"Mommy has to start radiation next week," I told them, as they sat with me on the couch.

"Are you going to lose your hair again?" Kalea asked, panic in her eyes.

"No," I said, putting my arm around her and pulling her close. "Nothing like that, but I might be really, really tired. Radiation is like an x-ray that zaps away my cancer."

"Like a superpower?" asked Kade.

"Yes!" I agreed.

"It zaps it into a million little pieces? Until it is destroyed?" Kade asked in an evil voice, scrunching up his face like some sort of villain.

Kalea and I laughed. Kade was too cute to be scary.

"I have to do it 28 times," I explained, and then an idea popped into my head. "We should make a countdown!". Both kids excitedly jumped off the couch.

"We made paper chains at school today! Can we make a paper chain?" asked Kalea.

"Yes! That's perfect!" I told her. "Great idea!

The kids and I rolled and stapled 28 links to make a colorful construction paper chain.

"There!" I said, as I hung it from a curtain rod in the family room. "Every night after dinner, we will tear off a link. When the chain is gone, I will be done. No more cancer!"

The kids clapped and cheered.

"Mommy's cancer is getting zapped!" yelled Kade in that evil voice. "Cancer will be destroyed."

* *

I pulled into the parking lot for my first radiation treatment.

"Twenty-eight days. You can do this," I heard Susan say in my head.

155

I went straight to the changing room to put on my balloon shirt. A soap opera played on the television in the waiting room. A water cooler sat in the corner, a stack of cups on top of the water jug. I picked a strawberry candy, the ones with liquid inside in a red and green wrapper, from the bowl on the end table. A partially completed jigsaw puzzle of a cruise ship sat atop another table. Pamphlets about cancer organizations were displayed on a shelf next to a box of tissues and a desk calendar. On the wall hung several posters with inspirational messages. I had sucked on the hard candy long enough to bite through it. A jagged ball of candy pieces stuck to my teeth when a woman wearing scrubs and a kind smile called my name.

"That's me," I said as I swallowed that mouthful of candy shards and stood up to meet her.

Her name was Ellen. I followed her down the hall to the radiation room. She introduced me to Todd, the other radiation tech. They positioned me on the table, lining up the 'x''s marked on my skin and walked out of the room. I closed my eyes and listened to the 80's music playing on the radio. As Boy George crooned the last few verses of "I'll Tumble For Ya", I heard the robotic machine move across my body. I felt heat and a weird, sort of buzzing or energy in my body. It was probably in my head. Just as a Madonna song began to play, the machine stopped humming and the door opened. The lights flicked on and Ellen velcroed my shirt back together.

It was over. It only took a few minutes. This first round was easy. It took longer for me to change into my shirt than it did to have the radiation treatment.

"Make sure you are careful with those Sharpie marks," said Ellen. We will see you tomorrow."

That night, after dinner, the kids fought over who got to rip off the first link of the chain.

"I want to do the first one," Kade said. Kalea reached over and tore the bottom rung from the chain.

"Hey!" Kade protested.

"You can do it tomorrow, Bud!", I said. "You get to pull off number two!"

"I get number two," Kade said to Kalea, "You only got number one."

"I got to take off the first one," Kalea said with her hands on her hips.

I distracted them both with brownies and gave Kade the first one.

"I got the first brownie, Kalea!" Kade said.

"Now you are even," I said. "Enough."

One down, twenty seven to go. I could do this.

I went to radiation every weekday at 12:30. I listened to 80's top hits on the radio while the radiation zapped my cancer and chatted with Colleen, Todd, and Ellen. I saw Dr. Kalani once a week. Other than a little redness to the radiated area and a massive amount of fatigue, everything was going well. Each night, we ripped off a link of the chain. That silly chain along with the kid's enthusiasm got me through that last leg of my cancer treatment.

On October 10, 2013, I drove to radiation for my final treatment. My cheeks hurt from smiling, and I almost skipped to the office. I grabbed one of those strawberry candies, changed into my balloon shirt for the last time, and hopped on the table.

"Last one, Jen!" Ellen cheered when she entered the room.

"Woo hoo! Tonight, I am taking a hot shower and scrubbing off every last bit of this Sharpie marker," I told Ellen and Todd.

"Do me a favor and wait a week or two to scrub it off," Ellen suggested. "Your skin is irritated. Let yourself heal first then you can scrub all you want."

I agreed. They positioned me on the table and left the room. While Mister Mister sang "Broken Wings", those robotic machines moved and hummed for the last time.

"Thank you for everything," I said. "I will stop in to see you sometime."

"You are done," said Ellen. "We would love to see you, but go live your life and don't think about this place anymore."

I gave them another hug and told them I would pop in next week at my follow-up appointment. I changed and met them in the hallway. Patients got to ring the bell when they finished treatment. I typically hated to be the center of attention, but I didn't mind that day. I tugged on the rope and the bell rang out as the staff clapped and cheered. They handed me a 'certificate of completion'. I hugged them and waved goodbye.

I walked out of the office. It didn't seem real. *Was I really done?* When I passed through the sliding glass doors, a beautiful blue sky with big puffy-white-clouds greeted me. I looked up and whispered "Thank You" to God. I stopped in the middle of the parking lot and felt the sun on my face. For 405 days, I endured chemo, surgery, reconstruction, and radiation. I suffered through pain and fear and personal struggles, but I trusted God to see me through. It wasn't easy. Praise God, I was done!

"BEEEEEEP!" a horn blared, interrupting my moment and making me jump.

I was standing in the middle of the drop off lane and holding up traffic. I laughed and waved an apology to the driver. He did not smile back. I took a few steps to clear the lane and stopped short again. Across the parking lot, my white Jeep was decorated with pink balloons.

"Look at that," I said out loud, as I took in the sight. Susan and Charlie left separate bunches of balloons tied to my car. I read the cards of congratulations and well wishes. With my backseat full of pink balloons, I turned on the radio and the American Authors song "Best Day of My Life" was playing. I turned up the volume.

It really was one of the best days of my life.

* *

When I got home, I discovered Mom filled the whole house with 28 more pink balloons, one for every radiation treatment. Bunches of pink balloons sat all over the first floor and more lined the staircase and the balcony overlooking the foyer.

Mike was traveling for work that day, but called to congratulate me. I told him how it went and about the balloons. He felt terrible that he missed my last day and worked an extra-long day so he could make it home for a celebratory dinner. As I looked at my family seated around the dinner table, not a trace of the last year on their faces. We made it.

Later that evening, we stood on the front lawn, all those balloons distributed between us. So many pink balloons! We released them into the heavens along with the pain, fear, and sadness they represented. Pink balloons twisted and turned up into the sky and out of sight. I said goodbye to cancer. For good.

Chapter Twenty-Two

My hands were full of LifeConfetti bags when I walked into the elevator. A professionally dressed woman, possibly a pharmaceutical rep, asked me about them. I explained they were for cancer patients and I was heading to the 5th floor cancer center to deliver them.
"Ugh. Don't you hate going in there? Everyone looks like they are dying. It freaks me out."

Rainbow houses, everyone!" I yelled into the back seat. The row of colorful houses along the bay were a landmark we watched for every trip to Ocean City, Maryland. The kids were sleepy but sat up and leaned toward the passenger side window.

Mike had a meeting with a condo association board and we tagged along for the weekend. The last time we were in Ocean City I discovered the lump. We checked in at the front desk and took the elevator to our floor. Mike and I stepped out first to see Kalea's face when she stepped onto the balcony.

"Whoa!" she said, her eyes and mouth wide open as she looked below. "Is that an ice rink?"

"It sure is!" said Mike.

"Kalea, there is an ice rink in the middle of the hotel!" Kade said laughing in disbelief, his nose pressed against the glass paneled railing.

We got a room at The Carousel, a resort hotel with an ice rink in the middle of the first floor. Kalea loved ice skating. It was late so we promised her we could skate tomorrow.

The next morning, Mike helped us carry all the buckets, shovels, and bags to the beach before he left for work. It was October, but unseasonably warm. A gorgeous blue-sky-and- puffy-white-clouds kind of day. I took a deep breath of ocean air and gratitude and played with the kids, chasing waves and building sandcastles all day. When Mike joined us later, I stole a quiet moment at the water's edge.

God, thank you for bringing me back here. I stood at these waters and prayed for strength and for more time with my family. Through it all, you were faithful. You changed my heart. You opened my eyes. And you brought me through it. I promised You I would spend the rest of my days sharing your Word and my testimony. I will keep that promise. Thank you for this trip and for providing the sunshine on this fall day so we can enjoy the beach together.

That night after dinner, we went to the ice rink. Mike skated with the kids for a while and joined me on the bench. We watched them as they waved and smiled at us with every lap. Mike didn't say much but no words were required. A knowing smile and a deep exhale said it all.

The American Authors song, "Best Day of My Life" played through the speakers. I grabbed Mike's hand. That song played on the way home from my final radiation treatment. There wasn't just one 'best day'. They were all going to be my 'best days'.

* *

I baked a batch of chocolate chip cookies while Mike finished some work. My final appointment with Dr. Kalani was that afternoon.

"I can't wait until this appointment is over. I will only have follow-up appointments with Dr. Mendez every 3 months!"

"I am excited too," Mike said. "Let's get this done and get out of here." We walked into the office, and Colleen called me back right away. I took the cookies to Ellen and Todd.

"Chocolate chip cookies are my favorite," Ellen said, taking the tray. "Oooh! And they are still warm!"

"Thank you for everything," I said. "Enjoy the cookies." I gave them another hug and went back to the room to wait for Dr. Kalani. Mike sat in a chair in the exam room, his head resting on the wall behind him. He looked deep in thought, or maybe tired. I hoped the appointment didn't take long. He was already behind on work.

"Hello, guys," said Dr. Kalani as he entered the room.

"Well, you did it, Jen! Twenty-eight treatments. Done."

He discussed the long-term effects of radiation. My skin was red and irritated, but getting better. The skin might be permanently darker in the radiated area, and would always be more sensitive to the sun. Sunscreen was a must. There was a long list of issues, but I didn't pay much attention. I wanted him to release me already.

"So, you had chemotherapy, a double mastectomy, and radiation. Your cancer can return, but Dr. Mendez will keep a close eye on you. We want you to live a long, happy life."

"Sounds good to me," I said, bouncing in my seat, so excited to close the door on the last year.

"What about you, Mike?" he asked. "Your wife will be around for a long time. How does that sound?" Mike was quiet for a moment. At first, I thought he didn't hear Dr. Kalani. He looked down at the ground and cleared his throat.

"Great," Mike said, his voice cracking. "I need her." His reaction caught me by surprise.

"I need her, the kids need her," he continued as he looked away, wiping a tear from his eye. I squeezed his hand. He had been a huge support for me, my rock. He stayed strong. He must have had difficult moments, but he hid that from me. Today, I didn't see my Superman. A man afraid of losing his wife sat beside me. Mike cleared his throat again and stood up to shake Dr. Kalani's hand.

"Thank you," Mike said. I stood up and gave Dr. Kalani a hug. We all took a collective deep breath, shook off the emotion, and said our goodbyes.

Mike and I walked out of the office into the parking lot to a beautiful blue sky peppered with puffy-white-clouds. This year had been heavy, but I could finally release that weight.

"I'm done," I said.

"You did it!" Mike took my hand and raised my arm like a boxer who just won a championship.

"We did it," I said. "Let's go home."

* *

"What book do you want me to read tomorrow, Bud?" I asked Kade as we sat in front of the bookcase in his bedroom. He ran his finger across the books, carefully reading the titles.

"This one!" he said, grabbing the oversized book off the shelf. It was a Dr. Seuss book called "What Was I Scared of", the one about the spooky pants 'with nobody inside them'. Halloween was a week away so it was a perfect choice.

His 7th birthday was tomorrow and I got to read this book to the classroom in celebration. We were both excited. I took the whole afternoon off to spend with him in his first grade classroom.

"Unless some sort of emergency vehicle is involved, do not call me," I joked with my staff when I left for the day. I used to rush to the school and straight back to work when something was going on at the school. I was the last one to arrive before the program and the first one out to the parking lot when it was over. I wasn't that mom anymore.

That night, we celebrated his birthday at his favorite restaurant. He ate more breadsticks than I thought humanly possible. When the waitress found out it was his special day, she brought him a big bowl of ice cream with a candle in it since he didn't like cake. He tried not to smile when they sang 'Happy Birthday' but he couldn't help it, his little face aglow with candlelight.

A week later, we walked through the neighborhood on trick or treat night, hitting both cul-de-sacs and every house on the way up the hill. Kade dressed as Charlie Brown in a striped yellow shirt and shorts. Kalea dressed as her American Girl doll, Saige, in a purple dress and multi-colored belt. The neighborhood buzzed with energy. Princesses and monsters and cartoon characters flooded the streets. The kids' candy bags got so heavy Mike had to carry them. The rain cut our night short but we had a great time. When we returned we had two tired kids and two ridiculously large bags of candy. The year before, I sat in our driveway with Mom while Mike walked with the kids. I went inside early, too tired and sick from the chemo.

"What a difference a year makes," Mom said.

* *

I stopped at the grocery store to pick up a few things on the way home from work. The cold November wind made me catch my breath. Zipping my sweatshirt, I put my head down and scurried to the door. I got what I needed and rushed out of the store. As I walked outside, I looked up to see the bluest of skies. No puffy-white-clouds, but clear and brilliant. I stopped short in the middle of the parking lot to take it in. I heard a man grumble as he darted around me.

Thank you God for this beautiful day and that gorgeous sky.

How did I miss that beautiful sight? Distracted by the cold and the task at hand, I never looked up. As I started the car, I noticed people heading into the store with their heads down. I felt sorry for them. They were all in such a rush, and they had no idea what they were missing.

* *

"I think this was one of my favorite Thanksgivings," I said to the kids on the way home from Mike's mom's house. It had been a wonderful day. My heart and my belly were full. The kids were already thinking about Christmas.

"Are we decorating tomorrow?" Kalea asked from the back seat.

"Yep," said Mike. "Your mom is going to make me put up a hundred trees and ten thousand lights. I'll be working all day." We laughed but he wasn't kidding.

"You complain, but you love it too," I said. He couldn't disagree. It was tradition. We decorated the whole house, a tree in almost every room.

Over the holidays, we spent many nights at home by the fireplace admiring the Christmas tree. We continued our tradition with a trip to Kennywood's "Holiday Lights". My favorite was still the carousel. The kids enjoyed the train and watching the artist sculpt snowmen out of ice blocks. I was grateful to walk through the park without stopping to rest at every bench.

In the middle of the Christmas craziness, we celebrated Kalea's 8th birthday with all things girly and sparkly. She wore a glittery pink sash to the restaurant that night. We came home and she blew out her candles on the ice cream cake she requested and opened her gifts. It was simple, and it was perfect.

"Mommy, the boys in my class are so bad. They don't even listen to the teacher. They talk when she is talking. They even get in trouble in the bathroom," she said, an indignant look on her face. As she rattled on about the atrocious behavior of the boys in her class, she took a big bite of ice cream. It fell off the spoon and rolled down her shirt into her lap. She never stopped talking while she spooned the ice cream off her pants and put it in her mouth. Yes, sometimes my heart ached over her growing up, but my little girl was still in there.

We continued the holiday traditions with our Collins Christmas Cookie Extravaganza, baking a gazillion Christmas cookies all in one day. We dropped off cookie plates to friends and neighbors. We made gingerbread houses, ice skated with Santa Claus, and snuggled on the couch for more than a few holiday family movie nights. We had a quiet Christmas at home.

We might have overdone it on the Christmas gifts that year, but the best gift was being there to celebrate with my family. I was excited to put the year behind me and to start a new one free of cancer. With a new perspective and a clean bill of health, we celebrated New Year's Eve at home with friends.

Goodbye 2013, hello 2014, a year without cancer.

Chapter Twenty-Three

fika *(fee-ka)*
Swedish: a moment to slow down and appreciate
the good things in life.

It had been a wonderful holiday season. We looked forward to spring but still had a stretch of cold, dreary weather before us.I made a cup of chamomile tea and sat in the morning room while I looked out the window and enjoyed the peace and quiet. Everyone was still sleeping. I spent some time with God, read my Bible, and gathered my thoughts. My schedule was cleared of chemo and doctor appointments, but also of committee meetings and networking events. I removed the extras that once kept me from my family, and I no longer brought work home. We sat down to family meals, helped the kids with homework, and relaxed in the family room. Evenings were the highlight of my day instead of the desperate quest for bedtime they used to be.

Adjusting to my 'new normal' wasn't easy. People still expected me to be their 'go to girl', but I didn't say 'yes' to everything anymore. I didn't want to. Everytime I said, "yes" to them, I said, "no" to my family. I fought a daily battle to resist the urge to perform, to prove to the world, and maybe myself, I could do it all. Maybe joining one committee wouldn't be too much. Maybe I could help with those projects. After the kids went to bed, of course. My old ways poked through from time to time, but I made a promise. I was never going back to the way things were. I kept my eyes on God, my heart focused on my family, and my priorities straight.

I heard giggling followed by what sounded like a herd of elephants coming down the steps. I took another sip of tea before walking to the kitchen to greet them all a good morning.

They sure were a motley crew. My people were a mess of mismatched pajamas, crazy bedhead, and pillow marks on their faces. They were a sight to see, but they were all mine.

"Who wants pancakes?"

* *

"Do we really need two boxes of those?" Mike asked, looking in the cart that was already packed with a ton of snack items. We were shopping for all the "dippers" for fondue night on Valentine's Day.

"It's probably all too much, but I don't care. It's Valentine's Day and I'm not stuck upstairs in pain, flat on my back," I said.

"Fill it up," Mike said. "Get whatever you want."

After dinner, the kids sat at the counter watching intently as I arranged the overabundance of dippers. I pretended not to notice as they snatched rice crispy treats and strawberries off the plates. They looked adorable wearing festive headbands with light-up hearts. They each held the stuffed animals they got in their Valentine's Day gift bags.

"Chocolate is ready!"Mike said, placing the melted chocolate on the counter. I passed out the fondue sticks and the heart-covered paper plates but all three of them used their hands. Within seconds, both kids had chocolate all over their mouths and chins.

"Let me take these," I said, placing the stuffed animals safely on the other counter. I picked up a strawberry, and dipped it in the chocolate. It was as delicious as that moment. The kids got chocolate all over their faces, the counter, and their pajamas. What a mess. A beautiful mess.

"This is the best Valentine's Day ever!" yelled Kade.

"It sure is, Bud!" I said, wiping a big gob of chocolate off his forehead and licking it off my finger. Mike hugged me from behind, kissed my cheek, and said, "Happy Valentine's Day!"

Bud was right. Best Valentine's Day ever.

* *

The gym echoed with the sound of dozens of basketballs bouncing off the gym floor. We made our way up to the top row of the bleachers. Kalea was standing in the middle of the gym with a large group of girls. She looked up and waved. This was her second year playing basketball, but I couldn't go to any of her games last year. This year, I went to all of them. Tonight was her basketball shootout.

When it was her turn, she stood on the line and took her first shot. She missed. She took another shot and missed again. Her face fell. I wanted to run down on the court and tell her it was okay. She looked up at me, and I knew she was about to cry. I smiled and waved, encouraging her to try again. Mike made a gesture with his hand and nodded. She took another shot.

She made it!

Then she made it again. And again. And again. With a confident smile plastered across her face, she kept shooting and sinking them into the basket. When the buzzer screamed the time was up, we all jumped up and cheered.

She won!

It felt like a movie. Mike ran down the bleachers, gave her a high-five, and scooped her up in a big daddy bear hug. It wasn't the Olympics or a national championship, but it didn't matter.

She won, and I was there to see it.

Thank you, Lord.

* *

After I finished with a tour of the center, I sat down to work on the schedule when I heard the doorbell ring. I heard Jenn let someone in.

"Hello, Miss Jennifer," said Mrs. Hickman. "I have to get the girls for their appointments. I forgot to let you know. I'm sorry. I'm a little early though."

"No worries. They are all eating lunch so no one is napping yet." I motioned for her to sit down on the couch while she waited for the girls to finish.

"Hey, I haven't seen you, but I am so happy you are doing well. We are all grateful to you and your staff. Things were a little crazy for a while but we always knew our kids were well cared for and loved here."

"Thank you," I said. "That really means a lot; more than you know."

"You know, I didn't want to bring this up, but we got the emails and heard some staff members complaining here and there. Some handled themselves in a very unprofessional manner. I was relieved when they all moved on. We knew none of that was true." I couldn't help but start to cry; those emotions still close to the surface. Mrs. Hickman jumped off the couch and gave me a big hug.

"I'm sorry. I didn't mean to upset you," she said.

"It's okay. I'm sorry I'm so emotional," I apologized.

"You have been nothing, but wonderful to me and my family," she continued. "I am sorry you had to deal with that on top of everything else." I grabbed a tissue and wiped my eyes.

"It just means so much to hear that. It was hard. I had no idea what people thought about me. It was embarrassing."

"Well, let me tell you this. I had many conversations out in that parking lot with several parents after pick-up. We all love you because you have been so good to us and to our children. We knew your heart and your character. We all knew better."

I hugged her and thanked her again before she left. I walked her to the door and then came back to the office. I shut the door and then collapsed on the couch to collect my thoughts.

"We knew your heart and your character," her words echoed in my head.

That was my prayer in the kitchen that night. I prayed for God to help me through that mess. I prayed that my character would speak louder than their words.

God was always faithful.

Chapter Twenty-Four

"We must let go of the life we have planned, so as to accept the one that is waiting for us."

JOSEPH CAMPBELL

You want to meet us at the Springhouse?" Susan asked. She and Chrissie were helping out at the school and finished early. The Springhouse was one of our favorite lunch spots. It was a restaurant on a local farm. Something about it reminded me of home. I grew up right next to a farm, the cornfields were my playground.

"I can do that," I said. It was a slow day at the center. "I have to wrap a few things up at the center then I will head over. I'll meet you there."

I wasn't always able to meet them, but I did when I could. I was happy to leave a little early. I had an annoying cough. I hoped I wasn't getting sick. There were so many things going around the center and the kids were passing things back and forth at school. According to my last bloodwork, my white cell counts were normal, but my body was still run down.

"I'm sorry I'm late," I said as I slid into a booth next to Chrissie. "I had a phone call and a toddler emergency."

"It's okay," said Chrissie. "Glad you could make it. You couldn't come the last time."

"Yeah, I liked 'Chemo Jen' better," said Susan. I looked at her, confused. "'Chemo Jen' was available all the time." Susan looked serious for a moment and then busted out laughing.

We had a great lunch of home cooked foods and desserts and headed to the school to pick up the kids. We sat on the bench outside the school entrance waiting for dismissal time.

"What's that cough about?" Susan asked, concerned.

"I think I am getting a cold. So many things are going around the center," I said.

"You better take some Vitamin C," said Chrissie. "Or garlic! That's supposed to help keep you from getting a cold." Susan and I looked at her like she was crazy.

"It's true. Garlic helps keep away colds!"

The doors opened and the kids came out of the school. Bombarded with backpacks, lunchboxes, and stray papers, we gathered our kids and said our goodbyes.

"Go home and rest," said Susan, then added, laughing. "Or go eat a clove of garlic. Whatever Chrissie said."

"Shut up, Susan," yelled Chrissie as she walked away.

I loved those girls.

* *

Over the next few months, my cough grew worse. After my radiation treatments, I developed a dry, annoying cough that came and went. Every symptom brought fear that the cancer returned. Maybe because the worsening of the cough was so gradual, I didn't think much of it. Dr. Mendez noticed it at a follow-up appointment.

"It is probably nothing,'' my oncologist said. "But we have to know for sure. It could be a side effect from your radiation. I'll send you for a scan to make sure everything is okay."

I nodded in agreement, took the script, and left. I didn't want to do this again. I didn't want an IV, or a scan. I didn't want to wait for the results. That wasn't the worst part. What if the cancer was back?

"I don't want to do this again," I cried to Mike over the phone on the way home.

"I know," said Mike. "I don't either, but you have to get this figured out. It doesn't mean it is cancer. Let's go get the scan and then you will feel better."

The hospital called later that day and my scan was scheduled for the next evening. Mike drove to the outpatient center. Hearing the sounds of the machine again made me sick to my stomach. I was shaken, but I got through it. When it was over, we went to dinner and stopped at the bookstore. It was like date night. Almost. Exhausted from the emotions of the day, I went to bed early, but I couldn't sleep. I was terrified Dr. Mendez was going to tell me my cancer was back.

The next morning, the kids went off to school and I made a cup of tea. I had a million things to do but I sat at the kitchen counter, wondering when Dr. Mendez would call.

"Hey! What's going on?" Mike said, walking up behind me and rubbing my shoulders.

"I'm nervous," I said. "Waiting for Dr. Mendez to call."

"It will be okay," Mike said. "Maybe you need an antibiotic. He will call. Everything is going to be okay." His dismissive comment made me angry. He meant well, but he had no idea how I felt; how scary this was for me. I tried to swallow my emotions but the stress of the last few days forced them out.

"You don't know that," I said. "That is easy for you to say. It doesn't affect you."

"What?" Mike asked, moving to look me in the eyes. "This doesn't affect me? Really? No, I don't have cancer, but don't ever say this doesn't affect me. This affects me. This affects the kids. This affects all of us."

He was right. He was absolutely right. I let my emotions get the best of me. Mike was only trying to comfort me. He was as scared as I was.

"I'm sorry," I said. "You are right. This affects all of us, not just me. It is hard waiting for a phone call that is either really good, or really bad."

"I know," Mike said as he gave me a hug from behind. "I get it, but we are all in this together."

Later that morning, Dr. Mendez called and said my scans were clear. The cough was probably a lingering side effect from radiation to the chest wall. If it didn't get better, he would send me to an ENT specialist. It took the rest of the day for my nerves to settle, but everything was okay; just like Mike predicted.

"Phew!", said Mike. "Now we can all go back to normal." I wasn't sure what normal was anymore, but praise God, it wasn't cancer.

* *

"I signed Kade up for karate," Mike said when he came home, dropping a folder on the counter. "I am taking him tomorrow after school for his first private class."

"When did you do that?" I asked, confused. "What brought that on?"

During one of Kalea's softball games, Kade played with a few other siblings from her team as we sat in chairs near the playground. As we packed up after the game, a woman mistakenly thought Kade threw rocks at her young daughter. She approached Kade, grabbed him, and yelled in his face. We didn't see this happen, but my daughter and her friends did. Both kids were too upset to tell us until we left the field. On the way home, they started crying and explained what happened. We were angry, and Kade was traumatized.

Kade was shaken over the incident, referencing it over the next few weeks. We were concerned. Mike signed him up for karate classes because he wanted Kade to be able to defend himself. I had mixed emotions, but Mike convinced me it was a good idea. We thought it would help him gain some confidence.

He grew so much in the months following that first class. He was still shy and quiet, but he earned his white, yellow, and orange belts already. Today, he would earn his green belt.

I stood against the wall at the karate studio. Kade stood in line with the other children. Nervous, he adjusted and readjusted his shirt. During the promotion ceremony, Master Kelly congratulated the children on their hard work and accomplishments. When it was Kade's turn, Master Kelly stood in front of him as he tied the new green belt around his waist.

"Kade, who is giving you this belt today?" Master Kelly asked. His instructor asked this question at every promotion.

"Me, Sir," Kade said in a whisper.

"Oh no," corrected the instructor, "Say it proudly. Who is giving you this belt?"

"Me, Sir," Kade whispered again.

"Who?" he demanded. "A little louder."

"Me, Sir!" Kade said loud enough for the whole room to hear, as he held back a smile.

"That's right! You did this. You earned this belt," he said. "You should be very proud of yourself." A confident smile erupted on Kade's face. My mama heart was bursting with pride.

"Great job, Buddy!" I said when he brought me his certificate after the ceremony.

"Thank you, Mommy! I got my green belt," he said.

"I see that. I am so proud of you!"

"Thank you for coming," he said, giving me a big hug. I remembered those nights, watching him sleep, praying I'd be here for days like this. I squeezed him and felt his hair on my cheek and his breath in my ear. I didn't want to let him go.

"Oh, Buddy. I wouldn't miss this!"

* *

I cleaned up dinner as the kids sat at the kitchen counter and got ready for homework. Kalea pulled a book about dinosaurs from her backpack. She flipped through the pages telling Mike what she learned about each one. He listened to her describe how big they were and what they ate.

"Dad," she said, scrunching up her eyebrows in thought, "How old are you?"

"Old," Mike said. "Why?"

"Were dinosaurs around when you were little?" she asked. I tried not to laugh as I finished the dishes, thankful I had my back to them.

"No," Mike answered in a wounded voice.

"Oh," said Kalea, "That would have been awesome."

"Okay, what homework do you have?" he asked.

Kalea pulled out a folder. She only had a spelling worksheet and a writing page. Kade had a math sheet. Mike got them started and I ran upstairs to grab some laundry. When I got back downstairs, Kalea was done with spelling and working on her writing.

"Mom I just made 'f' in cursive," Kalea announced. She said it so fast and it took me a minute to figure out what she said.

"What?" Mike asked, snickering, realizing right away what she said.

"I made 'f' in cursive," Kalea repeated loudly. Mike was laughing like a little boy. Kade didn't understand what was so funny.

"What's 'f' in cursive?" Kade asked, curious why Mike laughed. Kalea was mad that Mike was laughing, and didn't answer Kade right away.

"What's 'f' in cursive?" Kade asked again, louder and more angry, waiting for an answer.

Mike howled like a middle school kid. I was amused and annoyed at the same time. Kalea looked at all of us trying to figure out what was funny, afraid Mike was laughing at her.

"What's 'f' in cursive?" Kade asked again. His sweet face scrunched up in frustration.

"This!" Kalea yelled, holding up her writing sheet and putting it in Kade's face, "This is 'f' in cursive!"

Mike sat on the floor. He couldn't take it anymore.

"You are such a child," I said, shaking my head.

"What is so funny?" Kalea said.

"Nothing," I told her. "You made an amazing 'f' in cursive, Kalea. Kade, this is cursive writing. Kalea is practicing making a letter 'f'. You will learn this next year."

"Why does Daddy think that is so funny?" Kade asked, confused.

"I don't know, Kade," I said. "Daddy's old."

"Hey!" Mike said. We all laughed.

This was how it was supposed to be. This was family time. Mike was on the floor, Kalea on his lap showing him dinosaur pictures. Kade put his papers in the pockets of his folder and put the folder in his backpack upside down. His papers fell out and onto the floor.

"Let me help you, Bud," I said, gathering the scattered papers and putting them neatly in his backpack. Kade sat next to Mike to hear the rest of the dinosaur story.

An ordinary night. I was living and loving my in-between.

Chapter Twenty-Five

"So when you had your surgery and they took your boobs off, did you feel like you weren't a woman anymore? I mean, really, are you still considered a woman if you don't have boobs?"

FAMILY MEMBER OF A FRIEND

You have work to do?" Mike asked. I sat at the kitchen counter and opened my notebook and my computer after I put the kids to bed.

"No," I said. "I think I am going to work on the blog tonight."

I set up a blog on a free website and called it "LifeConfetti" months earlier. I uploaded a cover photo and created a few pages, but never did anything with it. I was adjusting to life after cancer. I wanted to share my story but was hesitant to dive into those emotions.

That night, I wrote a blog post about the night Kalea won the basketball shoot-off and Kade's green belt promotion at karate. I was grateful to be alive and present. I wanted to encourage people to stop missing out on those precious moments. I called it "Here!".

I promised God I would tell my story, and my story was His story. After I poured my feelings into the keyboard, I wasn't sure I could do it. Could I put my heart out into the universe?

Lord, I want to share my experience and what I learned through this trial. I promised I would use the rest of my time to glorify you. My world fell apart and you put me back together. I hope to share what I learned through my mess. Let my words touch their hearts and draw them closer to you. Even if just one person.

I clicked "Publish". No more hesitation. I wasn't going to do that anymore.

* *

During a follow-up visit, I sat in the waiting room for a long time. I remembered when Dr. Mendez spent over an hour writing notes and answering all my questions at my first appointment. Someone else probably received bad news today. I settled back into my chair and opened my book. Dr. Mendez could take as long as he needed.

An older gentleman using a walker entered the room, wearing a ball cap on his bald head, a blue flannel shirt, and jeans held up by a belt buckled on the smallest hole so the end of the belt stuck straight out past his body. An oxygen tank hung from his shoulder and banged against his walker with every step. He checked in and took a seat at the puzzle table. He looked sad and lonely. I felt God tapping me on the shoulder. Should I go talk to him? After a few moments of hesitation, I stood up to join him at the puzzle table. No more hesitation. I promised.

"Jennifer!" the nurse called at the door. I wasn't sure what to do.

"This way," the nurse called. I looked back at the frail old man and went with the nurse, my heart heavy.

After my appointment, I checked the waiting room, but he was gone. I regretted my hesitation. I said I wouldn't do that anymore. I cried on the way home in the car, his sadness and loneliness felt in my heart.

God, forgive me. I wanted to talk to that man. I hesitated and missed my opportunity. I will never do that again. I will never miss another chance to offer my time, my ear, or my heart. I want to help people. Heidi told me her patients are so lonely. Some have no hope, no support system. I want to do something for them. Show me what to do, Lord.

* *

"Let's have a party. You guys want to come over tomorrow?" I asked Susan. We met at the park with the kids. Chrissie was away for the weekend with her family. We had no plans for that late summer evening.

"Sure," said Susan. "We aren't doing anything."

"Okay," I said, my mind racing. "Let's have an end of summer party? We can have pizza and games for the kids!"

The next day, I went to the party store and bought brightly colored plates and table covers, napkins, and even balloons. I bought candy and made treat bags for the kids. My house looked like Chuck E. Cheese.

"You asked us over for dinner," said Susan, laughing. "You didn't have to do all this."

"I know," I said. "I figured I might as well go all out. We are celebrating the end of summer. Let's do it right!"

We had a great time. The next morning I was packing away the extra party supplies and it hit me. It was over the top. I wanted to celebrate everything. Not just holidays. I celebrated the last day of school, the first day of summer, even the last softball game of the season or another lost tooth. I had theme parties. Make-your-own-pizza parties. Decorate-your-own- cookie parties.

Life didn't have to be a big party. What was I doing? I celebrated away my fear. Through treatment, I focused on getting better. Chemo, *check*. Surgery, *check*. Radiation, *check.* I had something to do. I had to survive. Now it is over, but the adrenaline, fight, and emotions were still in there. I didn't know what to do with them. We could celebrate when necessary, but I didn't have to celebrate every moment to prove I was still here. I already knew it was those in-between moments between the big events that were the best moments.

"Go big, or go home," I said. Turns out, I wanted to go home.

* *

I stopped planning parties, but I wanted to celebrate Mike. I wanted to thank him, but nothing seemed good enough. When we lived in Northern Virginia, Mike played in three local softball leagues. Almost every night, he came home from work and headed to a game. We moved to Pennsylvania and he started coaching youth baseball. When our kids were old enough to play, he coached their teams. Every year, I bought him the official MLB rule book and he read it for fun. We had a season ticket plan for the Pittsburgh Pirates. Mike loved baseball.

While at a Pirates game one night, an advertisement for the Pittsburgh Pirates Fantasy Camp at PNC Park was announced over the speakers.

"That would be awesome," Mike said after watching a promotional video on the big screen. I called the next day.

"I was booked until this morning. Someone just canceled," the organizer said. "If you want the spot for your husband, it's his! You got lucky. Caught me at just the right time." He called me lucky, but God reserved that spot just for Mike.

I signed him up, but asked the organizer for some time before he added him to the email list. I sent Mike on a ridiculous scavenger hunt. The last clue brought him back home. I handed him an envelope decorated with a home plate with the camp welcome letter inside.

"What?" he asked in disbelief. "I called a while back, and they said it was booked."

"I have my ways," I said. "You so deserve this."

Mike gave me a big hug and thanked me over and over again. For the next few weeks, he talked about it nonstop. The night before the first day, Mike printed out the release forms and camp schedule, packed his bag, and made sure he had everything.

"I can't sleep," he said in bed that night. "I'm too excited."

"I'm excited for you."

"Best wife ever," he said, grabbing my hand.

"Best husband ever."

Mike was not a morning person, but was showered and ready to go before I woke up the kids for school. Later that morning, he texted a picture of his Pirates uniform with "COLLINS" and his number "9" embroidered on the back, hanging in a locker at PNC Park. Under the picture, he texted, "This is awesome! Love you."

Later, the kids and I headed downtown on a gorgeous fall night in the city. We arrived at PNC Park and walked up the stairs to the concourse. PNC Park was a beautiful ballpark, showcasing the City of Pittsburgh, with a view that looked like a postcard. The curved cables on the gold Clemente Bridge highlighted the straight lines of the cityscape. An eclectic mix of old and modern buildings stood proudly on the other side of the river against the blue evening sky. I stole a moment to take in the incredible view, but the kids wanted to find Mike.

"Let's go!" Kade said as he ran down the stadium steps, searching the field for his daddy.

"There he is!" yelled Kade, pointing to the edge of right field. Kade found him right away. He wore an official Pirates uniform and was warming up with the team. He looked great!

"Daddy, Daddy!" yelled the kids, as they waved their arms to get his attention. The stadium was empty. He heard them and ran toward us. We walked down the bleachers behind the dugout to meet him. He gave us all a bear hug and told us to sit behind the third base dugout since he was playing third base. When his coach called all the players back, he waved goodbye and ran to meet his team. I hadn't seen him that happy in a long time.

We picked our seats and the big screen lit up as the players took the field. The announcer introduced all the players as their pictures appeared on the screen, just like they were in the big leagues. When Mike's name was announced and the kids saw his picture, they erupted in cheers and jumped up and down. I was bursting inside.

"Mommy, stop crying!" Kalea scolded and rolled her eyes. She hated to see me cry, even happy tears. We watched Mike play baseball on a major league field. For the rest of the weekend, Mike stepped into the life of a professional baseball player. He had access to trainers and coaches, all the food and drinks he wanted, and he got to hang out with former Pirates players. During one of the last games, Mike even got to pitch from the pitcher's mound.

I tried to watch the games, but I rarely took my eyes off of Mike. He smiled every second out on the field as he lived out his boyhood dreams. I could never repay Mike for all he did for me, but this was about as close as I could get.

Chapter Twenty-Six

"Boy, people are making you dinner and giving you gifts?
Maybe I should get cancer."

AN ACQUAINTANCE AFTER I EXPRESSED HOW WONDERFUL
EVERYONE HAD BEEN TO ME AND MY FAMILY

Brush your teeth and put on your shoes," I yelled from the kitchen. The kids were playing around and we were going to be late for school. When my phone rang, it was my childhood friend Felicia. I ran upstairs to take the call.

"Mom has cancer," she told me. My heart sank. Jo was like a second mother to me growing up. Felicia and I had been friends our entire lives. We took dance lessons together. We were track stats and majorettes together. We giggled nonstop and created silly handshakes. We got into all kinds of mischief and Jo just shook her head. My dad and Jo were great friends too, sharing the same wit and feisty attitudes.

"Felicia, I am so sorry," I said. Felicia lived in Philadelphia, but her Mom still lived in Ford City, the small town where we grew up. Felicia had been traveling back and forth, taking care of her mother and the twin boys her mother adopted after Felicia went to college. Felicia worked full-time and had young twins of her own.

I reached out to Jo later that evening. We talked a little while but Jo was very sick. We promised to keep in touch so I could cheer her on through her treatment. A few weeks later, Felicia called to tell me Jo was in a Pittsburgh hospital and she was coming home that weekend. I made plans to meet her at the hospital.

When I arrived, Jo was alone in her hospital room. We talked about anything and everything. Jo was a single mother. She raised Felicia on her own with the help of Felicia's grandparents. She was a strong, independent woman. She worked full-time as a social worker and attended school at night to earn her master's degree. Jo was fearless. Her job was to protect the children and she did, even when her personal safety was threatened. Jo put up with our shenanigans, but when she gave us 'that look', we knew she had enough. Knowing the powerful force she was, it was difficult to see her looking so tired and frail.

After Felicia went to college, Jo could have enjoyed her empty nest years. Instead, she adopted twin boys with special needs. She fought for those boys like she fought for the children she protected over the years, making sure they had every opportunity they deserved. As she told me about how well the boys were doing at school, a social worker knocked on the door.

"Is it okay to discuss this now?" the social worker asked, glancing at me. Jo followed her gaze and quickly answered, "Oh, it's fine. She can be here. That's my daughter's friend. She's family."

Jo calling me 'family' was an honor. I watched her sign her name on a bunch of documents. In a cancer scarf and a hospital gown, Jo was still taking care of others. Going through the most difficult time in her life, Jo was more concerned that her boys would be alright.

When Felicia came in, I hugged my dear old friend and she felt like home. Felicia flashed that big smile of hers, but I knew she was hurting. She and Jo had an unbreakable bond. Jo and Felicia against the world. Now Felicia tried to prepare for a world without her. My heart broke for her. We visited for a little while and I left so they could spend time with their family. I hugged Jo and told her I would pray for her. She was moving to a hospital in Philadelphia so that Felicia could better take care of her.

As I walked away, I turned around one more time to wave and say 'goodbye'. I knew that was the last time I would see her.

* *

I was lying in bed trying to sleep when it hit me. I knew what I could do for the patients at the cancer center. The old man in the blue flannel still weighed heavily on my mind. I wanted patients to know some-one cared and they were not alone. God blessed me with a wonderful support system and I wanted to give back. My life was getting back to normal but seeing patients suffering at my appointments was upsetting. I wanted to do something. Each month, I assembled twelve bags with comfort items like socks, mints, and chapstick. I posted about the gift bags on my blog. Friends reached out and wanted to help.

Dad passed away in the month of February. To celebrate his birth-day that May, we dropped flowers at the dialysis center; one for every patient there. That act of service gave us something to focus on rather than our grief. He would have loved the idea for the bags too.

At Easter time, generous members of my church donated new Bibles to include in the bags. I dropped those bags at the nurse's station before my appointment. After I saw Dr. Mendez, I sat in the back waiting room to check out. A large man with an oxygen tank and a Steelers ball cap sat across from me. He had thick dark hair and wore a t-shirt and shorts. He fumbled with the papers in his lap and several of them dropped onto the floor. I helped him and we started talking about treatment, doctors, and how people changed when he got sick.

"Me and my buddies used to have season tickets to the Steelers games. We got pizza at our favorite spot or grabbed a few beers after the game. Best times of my life," he said in a thick Pittsburgh accent, then paused for a moment to do something with his oxygen tank.

"Anyway, I got sick, then I couldn't go. One of my buddies invited his brother to take my seat. Once, they gave the tickets away and came over to watch the game with me. They picked up a pizza from our favorite place. That was the best night!"

"Sounds like you have some great friends," I said.

"I did. Over time, they stopped coming. They don't even call to check in anymore."

"I'm sorry," I said. I could feel the pain in his words. "Sometimes, people don't know what to say. I have lost a few friends along the way too."

"What is that about?" he asked. "Now, I don't talk to anyone, really. I had a conversation with the guy who drove me here from transport services. Now, I am talking to you. That's the most I've talked all week."

"Well I am glad we ended up here together," I said, not knowing what else to say. My heart was so heavy.

"I don't know why the Good Lord keeps me around," he said. "But I have to trust there is a good reason." Before I could respond, the two receptionists called us both to the check-out windows at the same time.

"Nice talking to you," he said, gathering his papers and throwing his oxygen tank over his shoulder. "I appreciate you listening to me." He turned around and walked to the receptionist window on the right, and I went to the one on the left.

It didn't take me long so I hurried back to the nurses station and grabbed one of the LifeConfetti bags. I quietly placed the bag near the man's chair as he talked to the receptionist. He looked up from his seat and down at the bag, confused.

"This is for you. Remember God always has a good reason. So nice meeting you. God bless you," I whispered, waved and walked out the door.

Before I dropped off the bags that morning, I prayed over them, asking God to take these small gifts and multiply their impact. He was so faithful. God placed me in that waiting room that day, affirmation this was what I was supposed to do.

* *

Too tired to cook dinner, I picked up a pizza on the way home from work. I hoped the kids didn't have too much homework. Thankfully, we had no activities that evening. I was exhausted. I hadn't been sleeping well. My elbow had been bothering me the last few nights. I had to prop it up on a pillow to relieve the discomfort. A side effect of my medicine was joint pain. My hips and knees bothered me during the day and my elbow throbbed at night. That annoying cough came back too, probably because I wasn't getting enough rest and my body wasn't able to fight things off so easily anymore.

Things were getting hectic again at the centers. I was still digging myself out from the hole after my medical leave. Attendance was down. Finding good, quality staff proved difficult. I would have to advertise again for new teachers for the new school year. Working more hours than I wanted, I felt myself slipping back into my old ways. Overwhelmed, I often took it out on Mike and the kids. The house was a mess. I felt like I failed at everything. Every day, people told me how inspiring and how strong I was. I wasn't either. I was struggling. I kept telling myself things would calm down but they never did.

* *

A few months later, Felicia called to tell me Jo passed away. I made the hour drive to our old home town. Jo's funeral was held in the small Baptist church, the same church I occasionally attended with Felicia as a child. I remembered sitting in those pews during a summer revival. I listened to the choir and the congregation loudly sing and dance with so much joy, amazed at how different it was than my church, the United Methodist Church just a few blocks away. I loved how they called out, "Amen", "Yes, Lord", and "Preach!". I was mesmerized. The love for Jesus was abundant in that place.

Today, I sat in those same wooden pews and listened to the choir. I expected a solemn service, but it was clearly a celebration. We sang. We worshiped. We honored an amazing woman. The preacher and several others spoke of her heart, her strength and her life well lived. As a child, I looked up to Jo as a strong, smart woman who chose a career to help others. As an adult, I realized she dedicated her whole life to helping others. Both my dad and Jo were as strong as they were stubborn. They were also kind and giving. They were characters whose spirits would live on long after they left this earth. I wanted to live my life like that too.

* *

I sat in a chair in the back room waiting to schedule my next follow-up appointment. An older man with a ball cap and a cane came from the chemo lab. I stood up to offer him my seat.

"Oh no, young lady," he said. "Please don't get up. I have been sitting back there for hours. I'd rather stand."

We chatted for a few minutes. He told me he would be on treatment for the rest of his life. I wasn't sure what to say, but he continued.

"Oh, I lived a good life. No regrets. I want to stick around as long as I can, but I am ready to go when the Good Lord is ready to take me. I don't deal with nonsense no more. I do what I want. Spend time with good people. No time for anything or anyone else."

"Sounds like good advice," I said, noticing the lines on his temples made his eyes look like they were smiling.

"Not advice," he said shortly. "Just the way it is. You got to be happy, right? Otherwise, what's the point?"

"Jennifer!" the receptionist yelled from her desk.

"That's me," I said. "You take care of yourself. Have a good day."

"Always do. Make that decision every day. You should too."

Later that week, I took Kalea to Fired Up, a paint-your-own-pottery place. We both loved to paint and it was a fun way to check in with my baby girl. Kalea picked out a plate and I chose a mug. As I painted, my mind wandered to the gentleman at the cancer center and what he said.

"I make that decision every day."

I painted, "Choose Happy" on my mug. I would drink my tea from that mug every day. I sure needed the reminder. The upcoming fall was going to be full of changes. Kalea was entering 4th grade, her last year at the elementary school. Kade was going to a brand new school. Mike was traveling a lot for work. The first center was struggling with low enrollment and the second center was barely holding on. My joints hurt. My feet hurt from the neuropathy. I couldn't sleep due to the nagging pain in my elbow and my incessant coughing. I prayed to find peace again in my soul, my marriage, and my home. Things were starting to unravel and I didn't know how to fix them.

God, I'm slipping. I don't know what to do. I am worried about the kids and all the transitions. Mike and I aren't connecting. We never see each other. I can't get my head above water with work, or anything really, before something else happens. I need to refocus again. I have been so busy. I need to get back on track. Show me how to do that.

* *

"Get your shoes on, guys!", I said, grabbing my purse and my Bible. "I'll be in the car." It was the typical Sunday rush to church. Thankfully, we only lived two minutes away. Even if we left at 10:30 when service started, we could make it before the end of the opening song. That's how most Sundays started. Always in a rush. Life started to feel out of control again. Mike had a migraine that morning so he stayed home.

"Greeters are still out," Kalea said. "Made it!". I parked the car and we hurried inside. The kids went to Junior Church and I made my way to the sanctuary. Members of the congregation who attended the earlier service were still gathered in the foyer. I quickly stopped to hug and greet a half dozen people before I made it to my seat as the worship team began the first song.

I sat back in my seat, my body releasing the stress of the morning, my soul soaking up the music and the words and the peace in that place. Church was the place I let it all go, often wiping away my tears as I listened to the lyrics of the songs seemingly meant just for me. I took careful notes as my pastor gave his sermon. I often looked away when his glance met mine in the middle of the service, feeling exposed, as if God included a message to me inside his sermon. By the time we stood for the closing song, I felt lighter than when I walked in, feeling heard and seen and known. After the final prayer came the fellowship that naturally occurred amongst souls refreshed after Sunday service. I hugged and chatted, losing track of time. It could be ten minutes or forty minutes later when Kalea and Kade met me in the sanctuary, hungry and ready to go home.

"Can we go now?" Kade asked.

"Why do you talk to everyone after church?" Kalea asked.

"I know," Kade said. "It takes forever."

They were young and anxious to get home, but I soaked in every second of Sunday mornings. When my life was in chaos, it was at church where God put my pieces back together. Every week, I left there stronger and better equipped to face a new week, assured that things would be okay.

* *

After much thought and prayer, I made the difficult decision to close the second center. Even with just one center, things never calmed down. I hoped if I only had to focus on one center, I could get my business and myself back on track. Over the next few months, that dry, annoying cough was back and showed no signs of leaving. Sometimes, I couldn't catch my breath.

"You need to get that checked out now," Mike said firmly. "That cough is worse than last time. Call Dr. Mendez tomorrow, or I will. I am worried about you."

"Ugh. I have had 3 scans over this stupid cough. They have all been clear," I said. Anytime I told Dr. Mendez that I was coughing, he scheduled a scan. I didn't want to do that again.

"This is different though. You start coughing and you can't stop. It goes on all the time. I don't think you realize how much you cough. It sounds painful. You need to make sure everything is okay."

I reluctantly called Julie and set up an appointment with Dr. Mendez for the next day.

In the morning, Mike asked if I wanted him to come with me. I did not. He was only trying to help, but I took my fear and anger out on him.

"Make sure you tell him everything," Mike warned. "I will call him myself."

I rolled my eyes and left for the appointment. I didn't even say goodbye.

"What's going on, Jen?" Dr. Mendez asked as he walked in the door. He sat on the stool and opened my file.

"I have this cough again. Mike said it is getting worse and insisted I call you," I said.

"I am glad he did," said Dr. Mendez. He asked more questions about the cough and I answered honestly, still not thinking much of it. I had been here before.

"So tell me what is going on with your elbow."

"It is really nothing. It doesn't hurt right now. It is a nagging pain. I only feel it at night. I have to hug a pillow when I sleep on my side. It wakes me up sometimes, an annoying ache. Nothing serious. No shooting pains. It doesn't hurt to touch it. When it aches at night, I grab my pillow and go back to sleep," I said.

"Well, Jen. It is probably nothing, but you know I have to send you for a scan. I hate to do that, but with your risk of recurrence, we have to make sure everything is okay. It sounds like it is worse than it was last time we scanned."

I left his office and by the time I got home, the outpatient center called with an appointment for an evening later in the week. Mike stood next to me as I talked to them. After I hung up the phone, I looked at him and said, "There! You happy now?"

He rolled his eyes and gave me a hug.

"I'm not happy you are upset, but I am happy to find out what is wrong." I buried my face in his shoulder and cried.

Mike went with me to the scan. I was nervous but managed to hold it together. Once it was over, I wasn't mad at him anymore. Mike promised me dinner after the scan. We went for tacos. Tacos made everything better, right?

Chapter Twenty-Seven

*"I am not afraid of storms, for I am learning
how to sail my ship."*

LOUISA MAY ALCOTT

Hurry up, Bud. We have to go," I said, waiting for him to tie his shoes. Mondays were hard. We jumped in the car and headed toward his new school as Kade told me about his classes and teachers. I was happy and relieved he was having a good year. My phone rang as we sat at a traffic light waiting to turn. It was Dr. Mendez. I answered the phone without a second thought, almost forgetting about the scan after our busy weekend and crazy morning.

"Hi, Jen," said Dr. Mendez in a professional tone. Something was wrong.

"Hey, there was something on your scan, that pain you had in your elbow concerns me. I want to schedule a bone scan so we can see what is going on."

"What is it?" I asked, as the car behind me honked the horn when the light turned green. Kade sat next to me so I chose my words carefully.

"It could be any number of things. I can't say until it is confirmed. That's why I want to send you for a bone scan to make sure."

If Kade wasn't in the car, I might have asked him more questions. Instead, I got off the phone and drove the rest of the way to school in silence. We pulled up to the entrance and Kade jumped out.

"Bye, Mom. tLove you," he said. I smiled and waved at him.

"Have a great day, Bud. I love you, Little Man. I'll see you after school." I held up the drop off line to watch him disappear around the corner.

I picked up my phone to call Mike. Instead, I called Dr. Mendez's office and left a message with Julie to call me back. Thoughts bounced around in my head as I pulled into the garage. I never had anything but a clear scan. I didn't know what to think, but I had to get Kalea ready and drop her off at school.

I walked through the hallway and yelled up the steps, "Kalea! You up and dressed?", before I walked into Mike's office.

"What's wrong?" he asked when he saw my face. I could barely speak. I whispered what Dr. Mendez said as I held back tears.

"If my cancer is back, if I have metastatic breast cancer, I only have two or three years," I said as tears streamed down my face. I knew the statistics. There was no cure for metastatic breast cancer and the prognosis was grim.

"Don't say that," Mike said, standing up. "You don't know that." He tried to be strong, but I saw fear on his face.

"The kids will only be eleven and twelve when— "

"Stop," Mike interrupted me, putting both hands on my shoulders. "Let's find out more before we get upset."

Kalea bounced down the steps and headed toward the kitchen.

"Do you want cereal or waffles?" I asked, startling her as I walked up behind her. "I will make you whatever you want."

"You scared me, Mom," Kalea said, giggling. "I'll take waffles with lots of syrup."

I sat with her as she ate her waffles, swirling every piece in as much syrup as possible. She was getting so big. Growing up so fast. I pushed her long hair behind her shoulder so it didn't fall onto her plate.

"What's going on at school today? Anything fun?" I asked.

"Not really," she said. "I'm going to play basketball with the boys at recess today. I beat them yesterday. The boys thought they could beat us because we are girls, but we won."

"That's my girl!" I said laughing as I wiped the sticky syrup off her face. I sent her up to brush her teeth and Mike walked into the kitchen.

"I left him a message. I am waiting for him to call me back. I couldn't say much on the phone with Kade sitting next to me," I said. "He caught me off guard. My scans have always been clear."

Kalea came around the corner, showing me her teeth. I checked to make sure she brushed well enough. Her teeth were clean, but she smelled like maple syrup.

"Good job, Sweet Pea," I said. "Grab your shoes and your backpack. Let's go."

I drove her to school and headed to the center. I talked to Allie about a few things then left for home. I couldn't focus on anything. The hospital called to schedule my bone scan. It was the morning of our 15th wedding anniversary. What a way to spend it.

"That's okay," Mike said. "If you feel up to it, we will go to dinner that night. If not, we will celebrate another day."

"This is not how I wanted to spend our 15th anniversary!"

"I know," he said. "We will celebrate big on our 16th."

I went upstairs and collapsed on the bed. Could this really be happening? Could my cancer be back? I curled up in a ball, pulled Mom's pink blanket around me, and cried myself to sleep.

"You want me to pick up Kade today?" Mike asked as he sat down on the bed next to me.

"No," I said, untangling myself from the blanket to sit up. "I will go get him. It will give me something to do." I was backing out of the garage when Dr. Mendez called.

"Hello?" I answered before it had time to ring.

"Hey, Jen. What's going on?" Dr. Mendez asked.

"I guess I just didn't understand what you meant when you said there was something on the scan. My son was in the car so I couldn't really ask any questions."

"Something showed up on the scan. A shadow. We don't know what it is. The radiologist said it was suspicious. I'm going to send you for a bone scan to figure it out."

"So do you think it is cancer?"

"Jen, I don't know what it is. I won't know until we get the biopsy results."

He was as kind as he always was, but I was frustrated and scared. I asked questions he couldn't answer, just like I did when I was first diagnosed. I wouldn't know anything until I had the scan results. There was nothing else I could do, but wait. And pray.

God, why would you do this? Why would you bring me through all the cancer crap, give me a couple of good years, and then allow this to happen? Why didn't you just take me the first time? I trusted you. I had faith. And this is what it gets me? Cancer in my bones? I don't think I can do this again. I don't want to do this. Please don't make me do this again...

What started out as a quiet prayer in my head turned into a crying, screaming fit in the car. I was angry. I caught a glimpse of myself in the rearview mirror. My eyes were puffy and red. My straight hair, damp with tears, curled on the sides of my face. I was a mess. One light away from Kade's school, I wiped my eyes, cranked up the air conditioner, and turned the vents so the air would dry my face.

"You've got to get it together, Jen," I said out loud as I pulled into the school parking lot. When I got up to the door in line, Kade stood there smiling.

"Hey, Bud! How was your day?" I asked, smiling extra big as Kade opened the door and hopped in the car. We drove home like it was any other day.

Chapter Twenty-Eight

"These times were sent, not to break you but to make you."
G. POOLE

We got the kids off to school that morning and headed to the hospital. I sat in a beige chair as the nurse poked around to find a vein in my right arm. She inserted the IV and left the room for a few minutes. She returned with what looked like a small metal suitcase, pulling out a syringe from inside a metal barrel. After the injection, she told me to come back in three hours for the scan.

Mike and I went to breakfast. I typically didn't like breakfast foods, but I was hungry. No egg whites and wheat toast for me today. I ordered a stack of chocolate chip pancakes and a side of crispy bacon. I even ordered chocolate milk.

"Our anniversaries have sucked lately, huh?" I said. "Remember that awful trip to Erie?" "Yep," he said. "That was romantic, wasn't it?"

"Not as romantic as this one. I couldn't think of a better way to celebrate our 15th wedding anniversary than having a bone scan at the hospital," I said, making swirly designs in my maple syrup.

"Next year will be better," he said. I half-smiled at him, afraid to even think about next year.

We paid the bill and headed to the mall. Neither of us were in the mood to shop, but we ended up at the bookstore, where we often ended up on date night. Dinner and Barnes & Noble was a good date, a step up from Home Depot. We left empty handed and headed back to the hospital to the third floor. Mike sat in the boring blue waiting room chairs while I pretended to sleep on the hard table during the bone scan. About 40 minutes later, we left the hospital. I caught a quick nap before the kids got home. We ordered a pizza for dinner that night. I didn't feel like cooking, and neither of us felt like celebrating.

The next day, Dr. Mendez called to say the same 'something' they saw on my CT scan also showed up on the bone scan. Now I needed a bone biopsy to see what it was. Ugh.

"Is it cancer? Is that what this is? Can you just say it?" I said.

"Jen, I don't know what it is. That's why we will do the biopsy to make sure," he said.

"Is this a fact-finding mission or is this for confirmation of what you already know?" I tried again.

"The hospital will call to set it up. Then, I will call you and let you know what we are dealing with, okay?" he said. I was painfully aware he didn't answer my question.

I told my mom and some of my friends what was going on. They all said things like, "It will be okay" and "Don't worry. You are fine". I wondered if people believed that or if they just had nothing better to say. I always felt dismissed. Something like "That sucks!" would have been better. Maybe, "You must be going out of your ever-loving mind" would have been good too. I prayed to, bargained with, and cursed God all at the same time.

Please don't let this be cancer, God.

Are you kidding me, God?

Give me the strength to handle what comes next, God.

What did I do wrong, God? Why are you punishing me like this?

* *

I was in a pre-op room, a different one than all the other times, when the surgeon rushed into the room. He had a file in one hand, a pen in the other. Never looking up, he introduced himself and asked me to state my name and birthdate. I barely got my birth year out when he interrupted me.

"So what are we doing here today, Jennifer?" he asked impatiently.

"I am having a bone biopsy on my elbow," I stated as quickly as I could.

"Incorrect," he said as though he was a game show host or a haughty professor. "I am performing a bone biopsy on your shoulder, the humerus to be exact. Nurse?"

The nervous nurse ran up to the side of the bed.

"I'm going to need you to pull up a file," he said and they both left the room. A few minutes later, another nurse explained my pain was felt in my elbow, but it was "referred pain". The suspicious mass was in my shoulder, not my elbow.

Before she finished talking to me, the surgeon came back and announced, "Okay, Jennifer. I will be performing a bone biopsy on your humerus bone, which is in your shoulder, not your elbow."

I heard this guy was one of the best, but I didn't like him very much. I saw Mike wanted to say something, but he didn't. He didn't want to anger the man who was momentarily jamming a needle into his wife's bones. They wheeled me back to the operating room. Tears started to fall from my eyes and I let them.

"It's going to be alright," said a kind nurse, rubbing my shoulders.

A moment later, I watched a needle push something through my veins. The room spun for a few seconds and I woke up in recovery.

The procedure went well. It was over. We went home to wait for Dr. Mendez to call.

He didn't call on Monday, Tuesday, or Wednesday. When I didn't hear from him by lunchtime on Friday, I called and left a message. Still nothing. It was going to be a long weekend.

We kept busy with the kids. It was a beautiful weekend, so we spent some time outside. We went out to dinner and had a family movie night complete with popcorn and movie snacks. I fought back tears the whole weekend, but managed to have a good time with my family. A sense of dread sat in the pit of my stomach. I couldn't sleep on Sunday night.

On Monday morning, Mike and I took a seat in the corner of the waiting room. We pretended to watch the news as we sat in silence. My heart was pounding in my chest. Every time a nurse called a name, my heart leaped into my throat. In just a few minutes, I would find out if I was still cancer-free or if I had stage 4 metastatic breast cancer. Life would resume, or I would leave not knowing how much life I had left.

"Jennifer!" the nurse yelled. Mike and I jumped out of our seats and followed the nurse to the same exam room where I met Dr. Mendez the first time. I wondered if that was a bad sign.

"You can both have a seat. Dr. Mendez will be with you shortly," the nurse said and shut the door behind her.

Mike grabbed my hand and looked straight ahead. His leg was bouncing so he picked up my hand and moved it to the arm rest. I looked out the window at the church across the street. I noticed it was a blue sky and puffy-white-cloud kind of day. Those days seemed to follow me around. I took no solace in the beautiful day. Bad news came on beautiful days, too.

A few minutes later, I heard the familiar footsteps of Dr. Mendez and the slight knock on the door. Dr. Mendez entered the room, holding my file at his side, and staring at the floor. He let out a long sigh that told us everything we needed to know. Mike's chin dropped to his chest. Dr. Mendez sat down on the wheeled stool, the weight of the world on his shoulders. He slowly raised his head to look at us.

"It's cancer, isn't it?" I asked. I wanted him to say it.

Dr. Mendez took in a big breath and breathed out, "Yes, it's cancer."

I felt the wind escape my lungs. I looked at Dr. Mendez and then at Mike. A single tear fell on his cheek. I didn't try to stop my tears.

"Your cancer has metastasized to your bones and lungs," he said in an uncharacteristically technical manner, handing me a tissue.

"My lungs?" I asked, confused. No one said anything about my lungs.

"Yes. You have a cancerous lesion in your left humerus, your shoulder bone. You also have small spots on your lungs. They are too small to biopsy so we can't be 100% certain, but we are pretty sure."

"So what now?" I asked, wringing the tissue in my hands. "Chemo?"

"No chemo right now," he said. "I want you to go back to your radiation oncologist. You will have radiation to the shoulder bone. Then when that is over, we will get you started on a new treatment. Your systemic treatment should take care of the spots on your lungs."

"So I will lose my hair again?"

"No. You won't lose your hair. There is a new drug on the market that has been pretty successful. It is an oral chemo. It has side effects, but hair loss isn't one of them," he told me. I felt guilty for worrying about my hair.

"Once radiation is over, we will give you a shot in your belly that will shut down your estrogen production. We have to put you into medical menopause to take this drug. When your levels are low enough, you can start the treatment. We will talk about this later in more detail," he explained. "For now, go home and take some time. Call your doctor tomorrow to get things moving on radiation. We can't move forward with treatment until radiation is over."

I stood up, my legs shaking.

"We are going to take care of you, Jen," said Dr. Mendez and he gave me a hug.

We left the office, took the elevator downstairs, and walked outside. The puffy-white- clouds were gone but a clear blue sky hung overhead. My phone beeped. It was a text from Wilma, Mike's aunt. She had been diagnosed with cancer many months ago. She just finished her last chemo treatment.

"Congratulations, Wilma. I am so very happy for you. Love you!" I texted her back.

I got in the car and buckled my seatbelt. My friends were waiting to hear the results. How did I tell them the bad news?

"It's cancer," I texted.

The first person to text back was Susan.

"What can I do for you?" she asked.

"I don't know. Just pray for me. And be my friend," I texted back.

She texted back emojis of praying hands and two girls with a check mark next to them.

My phone started beeping as everyone received the message. I appreciated all the well wishes, but it was overwhelming. I turned down my phone, grabbed Mike's hand, and stared out the window.

I looked at Mike, and then down at our hands joined together. Mike held on so tightly. I knew he would always be by my side. I closed my eyes and shut out the world.

Why me?, I thought. Did I deserve this? I never thought this would happen to me again.

Lord, why did you bring me through this to throw me back in it again? What did I do wrong? Why are you punishing me? Why me?

God placed a message on my heart. *Why not me?*

Who else was more equipped to walk this path? I watched Dad navigate a dismal prognosis and suffer with grace and dignity. Mom loved me more than anything, wrapping her love around me in many ways. Mike would do anything for me. My two amazing kids inspired me to keep going even when it was hard. I had wonderful friends. For every friend who walked away, another stepped up to stand beside me.

Why not me?

Use me, Lord. You provided me with all the love and strength I needed to get through this. You showed me your faithfulness again and again. I had no reason to doubt, but every reason to trust. I know there must be a reason why. Everything you do is for good, even this. Good will come from it. If going through this will help someone else, then I will walk this road again. I trust you, Lord. Completely. I have to.

I opened my eyes and looked at the road before me and the deep ocean blue sky above. The leaves on the treetops danced in the wind as the golden sun sparkled and fell on the earth in rays. Orange tiger lilies, one of my favorites, peppered the roadside in a pop of color. I rolled down the window, took in the fresh air, and breathed it out along with the fear I carried inside me.

This was a hard day. My heart was broken, but there was still beauty all around me. I promised I would always look for it.

Chapter Twenty-Nine

"I won't let my pain turn my heart ugly. I will show you that surviving can be beautiful."

CHRISTY ANN MARTINE

Mike dropped me off at home and went to pick up the kids. While he was gone, I read through all my text messages. I couldn't respond yet, but I appreciated all the support.

"Why don't you let me take the kids tonight?" Susan texted. "Already talked to Giuseppe. We can order pizza and the kids can play. That will give you and Mike some time."

I didn't want to be away from them, but we needed it. Mike hadn't said a word since we left Dr. Mendez's office.

I took her up on her offer. Mike walked the kids outside when Susan came to get them. I wasn't ready to see anyone yet. He came inside and collapsed on the couch. I curled up on the love seat.

"You want to get dinner?" I asked.

"Yeah, we can do that," Mike said.

Neither of us moved.

"Come over here?" Mike asked a few moments later, moving toward the back of the couch so I could lie down in front of him. We used to watch TV like that all the time. He pulled a blanket off the back of the couch and I snuggled up against him. We always fit perfectly together like that. I felt warm and safe in his arms. I fell asleep. We both did.

When we woke up, it was dark outside. Neither of us felt like eating, and we didn't want to leave the house. I ate a bowl of cereal and made Mike a peanut butter and jelly sandwich. The kids would be home soon so we sat on the front porch. It was a beautiful fall night. The sky was crystal clear and the moon cast its opal-blue glow on the earth. Stars twinkled in the navy blue heavens. It was quiet outside, the only noise was the breeze blowing through the trees and up over the hill.

"I don't get it," Mike broke the silence. "You did everything you were supposed to do. How does this happen?"

"It just does, I guess."

"And you are a good person. You do anything for anybody. There are a lot of horrible people out there. Why did this happen to you?"

"I don't know," I said. I had no answers to his questions.

We both turned our heads toward the noise coming down the street. A dad and his son were walking their dog. As they got closer, I recognized them. They lived down the street. His little girl was recently diagnosed with stage 4 liver cancer.

"And that!" said Mike, pointing in their direction after they passed. "What is that about? That little girl getting cancer? If God is good, why would He let that happen? Why does He let stuff like that happen to good people?"

He was angry. I was saddened by his thoughts, but relieved he finally let out his emotions.

"I don't know why this happened," I said, looking up at those stars. I couldn't look at Mike. His eyes were full of sadness and a desperation I had never seen before. "I am not happy. I am devastated, and I am scared. I don't want to do this again. I thought I was done. I thought I was going to be that one who did the chemo, and the radiation, and never looked back. I thought I beat it."

"Me too," said Mike.

"I don't know why that didn't happen for me. In order to make sense out of it, to have peace in my heart, I have to believe there is a reason for all of this. I don't know what it is, but I have to trust God has a plan. Somehow, He will use this for good. I have to believe that."

"I don't get it," Mike said, shaking his head. "I'm too mad."

"Maybe me going through this will help someone else. There has to be a reason."

"I'm too angry right now to believe that," Mike said, looking off into the distance.

"I'm going to be okay," I said. Those words came out of my mouth with such confidence, I believed it myself.

Headlights approached. It was Susan with the kids. I couldn't wait to give them a hug. I heard the radio blasting and giggling before they pulled into the driveway. The kids jumped out of the car in a flurry of excitement, anxious to tell us all the fun they had.

Susan got out and leaned against the front of her car, crossing her arms in front of her chest. It took a moment before she was able to look me in the eyes. She filled me in on the shenanigans that happened at their house. I could tell she was about to cry because the moonlight reflected off the tears welling in her eyes.

"Don't do that," I warned. "If you do that, I'll do that, and I can't right now." She started to speak and stopped. She gave me a hug and squeezed me tight.

"Love you," she said, quickly wiping the tears from her eyes. She looked away, turned around, and got back in her car. She didn't have to say anymore. She said all I needed to hear.

* *

Before bed, I went upstairs to my closet and pulled out the box from the bottom shelf. I held it to my chest and crumpled to the floor. I set the box beside me. Dad's blue cardigan sweater. I buried my face in it, desperate for his familiar scent. It had long since faded, but I held it to my face and breathed in some more. Sobs erupted from a place deep inside. Oh, how I missed him. I opened the cardigan, slipped my arms through the sleeves, and pulled it around me. It was the closest thing to a hug from him I had on this earth. I sat back against the dresser and wrapped my arms around my knees.

When Dad was diagnosed with renal failure and started dialysis, he was placed on the transplant list and given a beeper the hospital would use if they found a match. One day, his beeper went off while he was out. Excited, he called back to find it was a wrong number. Even as he told the story, the disappointment showed on his face. I couldn't imagine the incredible high he must have felt when that beeper sounded and the low when that sound didn't mean what he hoped. As his renal disease progressed, his heart condition deteriorated. After one too many cardiac events, Dad was removed from the kidney transplant list. He no longer qualified, denied the opportunity for a chance to live.

I thought he would never be more disappointed than the day the beeper went off by mistake, but I was wrong. This was much worse. Sentenced to dialysis for the rest of his life, his life would undoubtedly be shortened. At the time, the magnitude of that disappointment escaped me. He didn't want to go to dialysis three days a week. He ached for a normal life. Selfishly, I thought as long as he had dialysis, he would live forever. I just wanted him here.

Now I understood how he felt. My cancer-free card had been revoked, my name no longer on the list, sentenced to a life of treatment, too. The rest of my life shortened. I admired my dad even more now and I didn't think that was possible.

When he learned his fate, he got knocked down, but got back up. When I was young, he spent his days at work. He was gone before we got up and often came home after we went to bed. After he got sick, he spent his days gardening. He sat on the porch and enjoyed the sunshine, even the rain. He was joyful. He was more kind, patient and giving. He was never in a hurry.

He pushed through his pain to help others. Family. Neighbors. Strangers. He drove dialysis patients from the other side of town home after grueling dialysis treatments so they didn't have to wait on the public van service. He recruited our whole family to buy gifts for the grandkids of a local convenience store clerk. On Christmas Eve, we drove to her house and left the presents on her porch. She knew it was him, but he never admitted it. Dad could have become angry and bitter. No one would have blamed him. But he accepted his fate and kept on living and loving. When my cancer came back, I didn't know what to do.

Turns out, I did. I learned it from my dad.

* *

"I hate that you had to come here again, but I am so happy to see you!"

Colleen said, wrapping me in a big hug. We went through all the paperwork and she gave me a new dignity shirt, one that was bubblegum pink. No prints or patterns, just ridiculously pink.

I met with Dr. Kalani and he prescribed seven radiation treatments to the left shoulder.

"Seven? That's it?" I asked. "I can do that!"

Since I had received radiation to the general area before, my risks were high for bone break and shoulder problems in my future. I didn't listen much to all of that. Nothing compared to the cancerous tumor growing inside my bones. I signed off on the seven treatments.

I was happy to see Todd and Ellen too. I joked they only remembered me for my chocolate chip cookies. I promised them another batch after I finished the next seven.

"Hey, Jen. I wanted to talk to you," Dr. Kalani said, stopping me in the middle of the hall after my fifth treatment. "I discussed your case yesterday at the tumor board meeting. I want to go for another four rounds of radiation. Eleven treatments total."

I wasn't sure what to think. What was a tumor board?

"See, you only have one lesion. You are young and otherwise healthy. I think we go after this aggressively. Knock it out for sure. Don't take this the wrong way, but I don't want to see you back here again."

"I'm okay with that," I said. "Whatever you think is best."

* *

After my 11th and final treatment, I un-velcroed my pink shirt and checked the skin on my shoulder. It was red but it didn't hurt. I survived treatment without any burns or issues. I changed and shoved the bubblegum shirt in my bag. Ellen asked me to meet her outside before I left. A few other staff members waited in the hallway near the bell.

"Here is your certificate," she said, handing me a document congratulating me for completing eleven rounds of radiation. "We wish you health and happiness. And we never want to see you in this place again."

"Unless you bring cookies," Todd added. They all laughed, then clapped and cheered.

"I'll bring those next week," I said.

"Would you like to ring the bell?" Ellen asked quietly.

I looked at the same bell I rang two years ago.

"No," I said to Ellen. It wasn't the same."I'll pass this time, but thank you."

"It's okay," she said, giving me another hug. "Most people don't ring it after the first time."

I walked out of the radiation center and got in my car. No balloons this time. As I drove home that day, I realized that this was my life now.

This was my life, for the rest of my life.

Chapter Thirty

After discussing metastatic breast cancer and my dismal prognosis, so many times I heard this from people...
"You know, everyone is going to die. We could all get hit by a bus tomorrow..." I hated when people said this to me. I hated it so much I googled the chances of getting hit by a bus. I already knew my chances with MBC.
Believe me, I'll gladly take those chances on that bus!

"So, you did it! Radiation is over," Dr. Mendez congratulated me.

"How do I know if it worked?" I asked. That question weighed heavily on my mind.

"We have to wait to do scans. The radiation stays in your body for a while so we will schedule scans in a few months." That didn't make me feel better, but there were rarely swift or easy answers when it came to cancer.

"I would like to prescribe Ibrance. It is an oral pill that is pretty new, but we have seen great results with fewer side effects. In order to take it, you have to be in menopause. I'd like to get you started on a monthly injection to bring down your estrogen levels. At a later date, we can look into ovary removal which will eliminate the need for the shot. With all you have been through, I don't want to put you through surgery just yet. You'll take Ibrance and another pill called Letrozole."

"So, two pills and an injection?" I asked. "I can handle that."

"Well, two injections. Since the cancer was in your bone, I would like to prescribe Xgeva too. It helps to prevent metastasis. It makes your bones stronger, but in a way, weaker at the same time. You will have to take Calcium and Vitamin D supplements."

"Is that the same as the shot I took after chemo?" I asked. "That was terrible."

"No," he said. "Nothing like that. One more thing, I would like to send you to an associate of mine. I want you to get a second opinion. It is a research hospital. They do clinical trials there. New trials come out all the time. I want to make sure there isn't something else on the horizon that would be a better fit."

"So, are you pushing me off to another doctor, then?" I asked, fearful this was a gentle way of breaking up with me.

"Absolutely not!" he assured me, smiling. "I just want to see that we are on the same page with your treatment. I respect this doctor and she keeps up with all the latest research. That's all."

"Okay," I said, looking at Mike. "Sound good to you?" Mike nodded his head in agreement.

* *

On our way to the research hospital, we drove through the Fort Pitt tunnel and were greeted with the amazing view of downtown Pittsburgh. The bridges, the buildings, the river. It was such a beautiful place. It was a shame we were heading there for a doctor appointment.

We parked in the garage and walked through a maze of hallways to get to the right office. It was a state-of-the-art building, but when we walked into the crowded waiting area, outdated chairs were squeezed together in the dark, cramped room. A broken magazine rack hung on the wall and a cracked water cooler sat in the corner. It was standing room only at the registration window so Mike grabbed the last two chairs while I waited in line.

"Next!" yelled an older woman as she slid open the glass. I stepped up to the window.

"Name?" she said, eyes on her computer screen. She grabbed a clipboard and a pen with one hand as she moved her mouse with the other, never taking her eyes off the screen.

"Fill this out. Don't bring it up here. Give it to them when they call you back," she said, shoving the clipboard out the window. "Next!"

I had to push past the backlog of people standing in line and squeeze between a side table and a display of information to get to the seat next to Mike. As I filled out the paperwork, a nurse shoved through the crowd and wrote "TWO HOURS" next to my doctor's name.

"We are going to be here all day," Mike said as he sat back in the uncomfortable chair.

The waiting room had no windows. The paint was a dirty blue color and was chipped around the baseboards and yellowed crown molding. Clutter sat in every corner. All the patients seemed miserable. They looked sick and uncomfortable, crammed in that tiny space. A sense of dread settled in my heart. It wasn't just clutter and uncleanliness. It was a feeling. I dug my phone out of my purse and texted Susan.

"I don't like this place. It is dirty and cramped, but I feel something bad here. I can't explain it. I can't wait to get out of here."

A few minutes later, Susan texted back, "I will pray for you. Maybe it's the Holy Spirit warning you about something. Trust that feeling. I hope all goes well and you get out of there quickly. Love you."

I sat there uncomfortably while Mike tried to read over reports from work. A wife was mad at her husband because he bought barbeque chips instead of plain. A woman held a child nodding off in her arms. Children in the toy area fought over a broken play-phone. A frail woman pulled her sweater around her, rested her head on the wall, and closed her eyes. People filed in quicker than were called back.

"Jennifer!" yelled a woman in office attire standing in the doorway at the other end of the room. Mike and I stood up, anxious to get out of the waiting room.

"You don't have to come," she said, pointing to Mike. "I just need her. Just some paperwork. She'll be back in a minute."

I didn't want to leave Mike behind, but I followed her into a small office in the back hallway. The woman sat behind a desk shoved in a corner. I took a seat, but had to stand to move my chair so I could shut the door behind me. Her desk was messy like the waiting room. She had short brown hair and wore no makeup. Her fingernails were bitten off and her white shirt had a few drops of coffee spilled down the front. She wore brown shoes that poked out from under the desk, but she did not wear a smile.

211

"Now tell me a little bit about your cancer," she said. I gave her my health history leading up to my stage four diagnosis.

"Hmmm..." she said with no emotion, "I'm sorry you went through all that. You know, clinical trials help bring new medicines to the masses. Maybe you should forgo traditional treatment and participate in a clinical trial. Do something for the greater good, help all the younger women coming behind you. You know, because this is kind of the end for you."

What did she just say? Greater good... Forgo traditional treatment... Younger women coming behind me... She sat back in her chair, arms folded across her chest, waiting for a response.

"I'm not here as a last resort," I said after a moment. "Dr. Mendez has a treatment plan for me. He sent me here to get a second opinion." She sighed as she sat up, tapping her pen on the desk. She set some paperwork in front of me to sign in the appropriate places.

"Okay," she said. "Go back to the waiting room. The nurse will call you when she is ready." She stood up and took my chair, folded it, and opened the door. She walked me back to the waiting room. "Good luck to you."

I stepped over toys some children left in the middle of the aisle and sat next to Mike.

"Everything okay?" he asked, looking up from his work. I just nodded. About an hour later, a nurse in scrubs called me back. She told Mike to wait until they called him back. I followed her to a room where she took my vitals. She was friendly, but complained it was a very busy day. She walked me to an exam room, placed a gown on the counter, and said the physician assistant would be in soon.

I changed into the light blue gown and sat on the crinkly paper on the exam table. It was cold so I grabbed my sweatshirt and threw it over my legs. After a quick knock, a tall, thin woman in a white coat walked into the room. Her blond hair was cut into a professional chin-length bob and she wore dark framed glasses on the end of her straight long nose. Like the first woman, she did not smile.

While she performed a routine exam, she was so quiet. I nervously filled the silence with chatter.

"I was so happy when Dr. Mendez told me I could take an oral pill this time. I assumed I would have to start IV chemo again. I won't even lose my hair," I said.

"Well, you know you have metastatic breast cancer. Eventually, you will have IV chemo. In the end, you will lose your hair," she said staring at me over her glasses. Her words penetrated my heart like daggers.

"For now, though," I managed, choking back tears. "It will be easier on my kids."

After the silent exam, she provided general information about the research programs at the hospital and about metastatic breast cancer.

"I know I shouldn't, but I googled MBC," I dared to speak again. "The prognosis was 18 to 33 months. Dr. Mendez told me not to listen to the statistics because they were outdated and new medicines were being developed all the time."

"That prognosis is correct. Only about 20% of metastatic breast cancer patients live five years after diagnosis," she said flatly. "The doctor will be in to see you soon. You can get dressed. Exam is over."

She walked out the door. I changed and sat down on a chair, fidgeting with the zipper on my sweatshirt. I was afraid to meet the doctor.

A few moments later, there was another knock on the door. The doctor walked in followed by the physician assistant. I didn't want to be in a room alone with them.

"Can my husband join us?" I asked, feeling like a schoolgirl.

"Sure," said the doctor. She had long brown hair and was younger than I expected. "Do you want to go get him?" she asked the physician assistant. "I'll go see the next patient and stop back in a few minutes."

A few minutes later, Mike came in and sat down next to me. I felt like I hadn't seen him in days. He grabbed my hand and I held on tightly.

"How is everything going?" he asked. Before I could answer, both women returned. The doctor introduced herself to us and opened my file. Her long brown hair was curled and resting on her shoulders. She wore glasses, but they weren't hanging off her nose. She was dressed in a hot pink top and a navy blue skirt under her monogrammed white coat. I could see her awesome strappy shoes under the exam table from my chair. She was professional, but kind.

"You have probably googled and seen some scary things online," she said, "Don't do that. The research is outdated." I glanced at the woman. She quickly looked down at the floor.

"There are new drugs coming out all the time," she continued, as Mike squeezed my hand. "The research was done years ago before these new advances were made. MBC is terminal. There is no cure. The prognosis remains the same. Eighteen to thirty-three months. Still, no one can give you an expiration date."

She looked through the file and said, "I have reviewed your case. At this point, we have no clinical trials that would benefit you. I agree with what Dr. Mendez has planned for you. Ibrance, Letrozole, and Xgeva once your estrogen levels have dropped."

She closed the file, wished us well, and walked out the door. I was relieved no trials were available. I never wanted to step foot in that place again.

"You're free to go," said the woman. "The exit is that way."

We walked out through the waiting room door. The room was still full of people. I felt so sorry for them. I would see Dr. Mendez next week. What if I came here first? What if this was all I knew? I was so grateful I had an oncologist who gave me hope. Hope that was missing in that place.

As we walked out of the hospital and into the parking garage, the heaviness of the day became too much. I opened the car door, collapsed in the front seat, and erupted into sobs.

"What's wrong?" Mike asked, pulling me toward him. I told him everything.

"They said all that to you? What kind of place is this?" Mike asked angrily.

"I can't stop thinking about all those people in the waiting room. They don't know anything different. How could they have any hope?"

"No wonder everyone was so miserable there," he said. "Don't listen to them. When do you see Dr. Mendez again? You tell him what happened. You tell him what they said to you."

"I will. I go next week. I don't ever want to go back to that place again."

"You won't," Mike said.

* *

I went to the lab and had a very large needle shoved into my stomach. It wasn't fun, but after all I had been through, it was doable. When I saw Dr. Mendez. I told him what happened. He was not happy.

"I am so sorry, Jen," he said. "I would have never sent you there if I knew that was going to happen."

"I am never going back there," I said.

"I'm never sending you back there," he said. "Let's prove them wrong."

Dr. Mendez explained the difference between treating early stage cancer and stage 4 cancer. In the early stage, treatment was aggressive, often harsh. The goal was to rid the body of cancer in hopes the patient would live long after treatment. With late stage cancer, the focus shifted to maintaining quality of life while keeping the cancer stable for as long as possible.

Every person responded differently to treatment. Patients were scanned regularly to check for progression. If there were no signs of progression, the patient remained on the same treatment. When scans showed progression, it meant treatment was no longer working. The patient might be prescribed radiation or surgery to deal with the progression; if appropriate. Either way, the patient started a new treatment plan.

Scan. Treat. Repeat.

This cycle continued until no more treatments were available or until the patient died. As a stage four cancer patient, I would be on treatment forever. I would hope for long periods of time when my disease was stable. I would live as normally as possible during the 'in between'.

"We are going to do our best to give you as much life, as much good life, as we can in between treatments," he said.

I already knew that "in between" was where all the good stuff happened. He told me what I needed to hear after that horrible day at the research hospital. Dr. Mendez didn't sugarcoat my diagnosis but he didn't point out my grim future. He treated me like a person, one who happened to have cancer.

Dr. Mendez didn't give me a death sentence. He gave me hope.

Chapter Thirty-One

When I called the specialty pharmacy, I had to answer a few questions before they would refill my prescriptions. They asked me about side effects and frequency of doctor appointments. Then this...

Customer service representative: *What are your life goals concerning your meds?*

Me: (confused) *I don't understand what you mean. Life goals?*

Customer service representative: (Frustrated) *You know, your goals. Like, what are your goals for your pills? What do you want to happen? Like, do you want to live longer?*

Me: *Uh... sure, put that.*

After two rounds of shots in my belly, my estrogen numbers were low enough to start Ibrance and Letrozole. Although Dr. Mendez felt my numbers looked good, my insurance company didn't. My insurance denied the prescription. My doctor was going to appeal, but I had to wait a little longer until they worked it out. I left the office in tears. I was afraid if I couldn't start treatment, my cancer would be left uncontrolled for too long. Those spots on my lungs were still there, untreated.

"I have to wait for the doctor to appeal," I said to Mike on the phone on the way home.

"That is ridiculous. How long is that going to take?" he asked.

"I don't know," I said, my voice cracking.

"We will figure this out," he said. "We will talk about it when you get home."

"I am on my way to pick up Bud. I will be home soon," I said, and hung up the phone. I was on the other side of town, but I would make it to Kade's school in time.

As I pulled into the pick-up line, I got myself together. I took a few cleansing breaths and waved in front of my eyes to dry the tears. Kade was walking to my car when Mike called back.

"Hey, your doctor is calling in that prescription. Call the nurse tomorrow and they will walk you through it. You have to order them through a specialty pharmacy."

"What? You mean it was approved?" I asked. "How did that happen?"

"I called our insurance and when I got a real person, she put me through to a supervisor. I stayed on the phone while she called Dr. Mendez's office and she told me it was done."

He saved me again. My Superman.

Because they were cancer meds, I could not pick them up at my local pharmacy. The drugs would be delivered to my home. When they arrived, I opened the package to find a purple and green pill box. The weeks were color coded for a four week cycle. I took both meds for three weeks and only 1 pill the fourth week. During the fourth week, my body would recover. White blood cell counts decreased during the first three weeks and the off week allowed my white counts to re-bound. I put the pills in the proper slots in the box and set it in the corner near my stand mixer. When did I become someone who had a pill box on her kitchen counter?

That night, I prepared to take my first dose. I had no idea how these drugs would affect me. If they would work. I filled a glass of water and held the two pills in my hand.

Lord, thank you for these pills, for the doctors and researchers who made this medication possible. My nurse said if I was diagnosed even a year ago, they might have told me to get my affairs in order. This drug came out just in time for me. Your timing is always perfect. I pray these pills work against the cancer while sparing my body the harsh side effects. If not, I pray for the strength to push through them. As always I pray for more time with my loved ones. I trust in you, Lord.

I popped those pills in my mouth and swallowed them. Over the next few months, my body adjusted slowly to the new treatment. Body aches, bone pain, and fatigue hit me hard. I felt very out of control. I didn't know if these meds were working. All I could do was take my pills, wait for my scan in about three months, and live my life "in between". This was my new normal. Nothing seemed very normal, but like Dad said, "You just have to keep going."

My family had to 'keep going' too. We told the kids my cancer came back in my shoulder bone. I had to have more radiation and take pills every day. Scans would make sure the cancer was stable. They didn't ask specific questions and took the news well.

It was fall again and Mike's "Old Man" baseball team, as we affectionately called it, was wrapping up the season. Mike wanted to have the guys over for an end-of-season party and I was totally on board. As the planning began, I hijacked his "Old Man" baseball party and turned it into a surprise party for him. I wanted to honor him as a father, coach, and a friend. I naturally changed the party to a Superman theme and invited local friends and some surprise guests from Virginia.

He knew his best friend John from Virginia was coming to visit that weekend. When they left to pick up the food, I filled the house with superhero decorations. I hung candid pictures of Mike as SuperDad, SuperCoach, and SuperHusband. A black cityscape was the backdrop for the dessert table that held Superman themed cupcakes and Clark bars. The best was the large Superman decal on the wall. I printed a picture of Mike's face and taped it on top of Superman's face. It was perfect. Mike was going to hate it.

I also bought a Supergirl shirt, a white button down, and a pair of fake glasses. When Mike and John got home, I met them at the door in costume and handed Mike a Superman shirt.

"What are you doing?" he asked, noticing my costume as he carried in pans of food.

"What is this?" he asked when he saw all the decorations and pictures. I watched his eyes travel to the morning room wall. His mouth dropped open and he turned to me.

"That is not staying up there!"

"Yes it is! That is the best!"

John laughed. Mike agreed to let it stay up for the party, but said it was coming down later that night. He went upstairs to change into his new Superman shirt before the guests arrived. All the "Old Man" baseball guys showed up and took turns giving Mike a hard time about the Superman decal, but it was all in fun.

About 30 minutes later, the surprise guests began to arrive. Every half hour, the doorbell rang and another surprise from his past showed up. Mike's face was lit up all night.

"You are the best wife ever," Mike said, as he walked up behind me, hugged me, and kissed me on the cheek. "I don't know how you pulled all this off. I will never trust you again, but thank you."

"Good thing you are pretty oblivious," I said, "Thank you... for everything."

* *

The holidays creeped up on me. I struggled to keep up with work and home while managing the fatigue from my medication. I was still reeling from the shock of my diagnosis. Work became more challenging. The center was not doing well. Attendance was down. I didn't have the motivation to turn things around. I resented the energy I put into caring for other people's kids instead of my own. I grieved the time I lost while building a business that would no longer exist. All the hours away from home seemed worth it back then while I chased my dreams. Now, those dreams didn't matter anymore. Giving up my career was a difficult decision. I closed the center in January, closing the door on my lifelong dream and career goals I made back in high school.

After years of putting everyone and everything ahead of my own health and happiness, I finally put myself on the list. I didn't know how much time I had left, but I didn't want to spend that time away from my family. God had a new plan for me. I had to be open to it. I had to embrace it. The decision came easier than I thought.

It was the right one.

Chapter Thirty-Two

"Occasionally weep deeply over the life you hoped would be.
Grieve the losses. Then wash your face. Trust God. And
embrace the life you have."

JOHN PIPER

When the center closed, I felt lost. What was I supposed to do with myself? What would I say when someone asked me what I did for a living? For months, I answered that question with, "I used to own child care centers". After some reflection, I stopped saying that. I had to figure out who I was now, but not having a job title was difficult for me. I slept the days away for a while.

"I cannot sleep my days away," I said to Mike one day.

"Of course you can," he said. "You are under doctor's orders to rest. So, rest!"

It wasn't that easy. I wasn't someone who napped. I didn't know how to sit still. I was sad and struggled with my new identity. I needed to feel productive so I started to clean and organize. I even redecorated. I picked new paint colors for the walls downstairs and once again, Mike made my vision happen. Bye bye, neutral colors. Hello, brights. Maybe it was my way of wiping out the old and starting fresh. I learned to give myself grace through this new phase in life. I did that with patience, and paint.

My nurse recommended finding a support group. I wasn't ready to join the one advertised on the bulletin board at the cancer center, but I found some stage 4 metastatic breast cancer groups on Facebook.

It was comforting to find others going through the same things, but it was hard reading about other patients suffering with side effects and progression. The worst were the memorial posts. Every day I saw a beautiful woman, often surrounded by young children in a family photo. Under the photos were comments like "Gone too soon" and "Fly high, Sister" along with a link to an obituary. It weighed heavy on my heart.

I tried to stay positive, even with all the sadness I saw. Sometimes I unfollowed the groups for a while. It was too much. An awareness project was proposed by one of those groups involving taking a picture on a pillow as though in a coffin and holding a sign that read "I am one of the 116 who dies every day from metastatic breast cancer". Although I understood the intention, I chose not to participate. My family would be upset if they saw something like that on my personal social media accounts. I thought it would turn people away, rather than educate. When asked for our opinion about the project, my feedback was not well-received. I suggested we take a more positive approach, drawing people in before educating them about MBC. Some were offended, saying I was 'too positive', which was often dangerous to patients like us. No one could 'positive vibe' themselves out of cancer. I never said I could. I was asked to leave the group. How about that?I got thrown out of an online cancer support group for being too positive. Ironic, huh? I dealt with enough negativity, just with my situation. I willingly left. No hard feelings.

I quickly learned very little funds went toward metastatic breast cancer. All those pink campaigns, all the pinkwashing that happened in October—they didn't help patients like me. The pink cans of soup, pink office supplies, and pink t-shirts with offensive sayings didn't help anyone suffering from MBC. Stage 4 metastatic breast cancer was the only breast cancer that killed, but not much was done about it. I became an advocate for MBC, educating friends and family when I could about the often misunderstood and overlooked disease. I learned that if we wanted a cure for MBC, we would have to advocate for ourselves.

* *

"Hey Jen, how are you?" I heard someone say as I looked for a good container of strawberries. It was my friend Erica. I hadn't seen her in a while. I gave her the condensed version of what was going on and we talked about our kids.

"Just know I am always praying for you. I put your name on our church's prayer list," she said as she gave me a hug.

"Oh, one more thing," Erica said, stopping to turn her cart around and leaning in close.

"Do you have any information about breast cancer support groups?" she whispered like she was telling an offensive joke. "My neighbor was just diagnosed. I mean, I know you could talk to her, but I don't want to tell her about you."

Chapter Thirty-Three

"We acquire the strength we have overcome."
-RALPH WALDO EMERSON

I was going to be 43 years old. Birthdays meant more these days. I wanted to host a small party for my friends. Show them how much I loved and appreciated them.

I had known Felicia, Kierstin, and Jennifer since elementary school. We shared all of life's milestones together.

Beth was one of my best friends. We were maids and matrons of honor at each other's weddings and spent countless Saturday mornings catching up on the phone even after I moved to Virginia.

I met Heidi on my first day of my senior year when I moved to a new school. She drew a map to my next class and invited me to sit with her at lunch. We shared all of life's big moments after that.

Jen was my dear friend who moved to California right before I was diagnosed the first time. Lynn was my neighbor, too. When I was diagnosed with stage 4, she cried in the car, telling me she would never be my strong friend, but would always be there for me. It was one of the most sincere things anyone ever said to me.

Wilma was Mike's aunt, but she was also my friend. We got through some rough times together, including cancer.

Melissa was one of my first friends when we moved back to Pennsylvania. She was silly and fun, and we always said we were going to start some side hustle together one day.

Susan and Chrissie were my newest friends, but they were my *Mom Squad*. I couldn't have made it through the last few years without them. Of course, my mom was my very best friend of all.

The plans came together quickly. As the guests arrived, the house buzzed with chatter and laughter. I introduced old friends to new friends. It did not surprise me they got along right away.

"It is surreal to have friends from different phases in my life here together in one place," I told everyone. "I am so happy you are here."

We had a great night. Everyone enjoyed the food and the company. They talked and laughed like they had known each other forever. They took turns telling touching, funny, and often embarrassing stories about me. At the end of the night, I passed out yellow gift bags to each of them.

"This is your birthday. Why are you giving us gifts?" Chrissie asked.

"I wanted to," I said. "Thank you all for coming, and thank you for being my friend."

I wrote a special card, pouring my heart out to each of them personally. I included some chocolate and a CD of "For Good" from *Wicked*, a song that expressed how my life was forever changed because I knew them.

We cut the cake. It was a triple layer round white cake with raspberry filling decorated with white and yellow flowers. It was sweet and simple and beautiful, just like those amazing women. These were my people. My circle. My tribe.

"This is delicious," someone said as they took a bite of cake. I looked around the room at all those lovely women.

It sure is.

* *

I found a seat in the corner. Kathy called me back for blood work right away. I set my purse and water bottle on the small desk and sat in the chair. Kathy put the padded bar down and I put my right arm on top of it. She tied my upper arm with two tourniquets and searched for a good vein. There was really only one.

"Okay, big pinch," she said. I looked away and she plunged the needle through my skin. It hurt, but only for a second. The lids clicked as she filled three small tubes with my blood. I returned to the waiting room and barely sat down before the nurse called me back to see Dr. Mendez.

"So, it's scan time again," he said. We are going to find out if Ibrance is working. We can check on your shoulder too."

The pet scan was scheduled a few weeks later. Mom and I found a small waiting room after I checked in at the desk. A kind tech named Randy walked me to a small room with a large beige recliner. He gave me the radioactive injection, similar to the bone scan, through an IV.

I relaxed in the darkened room for an hour before the scan. Everything went well, but then the waiting began. Mom and I stopped for breakfast on the way home. I got my scan special: chocolate chip pancakes and bacon.

"You should take a nap," Mom said when we got home. I did some light cleaning instead. I was taking a break for lunch when my phone rang. It was Dr. Mendez.

"Hey, Jen!" he said with an upbeat voice, "I just got your scans back. They look great!"

"Already?" I asked.

"Yes! I was about to go on my lunch break and your results came through. Scans look great. No cancer. And your shoulder looks good. There is a small hole where the lesion was, but that will take a while to heal. But good news overall. Ibrance is working!"

My cancer was stable! Praise God. *Hallelujah*.

Chapter Thirty Four

"In the end, it's not the years in your life that count. It's the life in your years."

ABRAHAM LINCOLN

The gym echoed with the sound of squeals and bouncing balls. I chatted with the other moms along the bleachers as Kalea ran around with her friends. The school held a big party for the fourth graders at the end of the year. Each student received a backpack full of gifts.

"Can you hold this?" Kalea said, handing me her bag and all its disheveled contents before running off to play.

I sat down on the gym floor to organize them. I folded the beach towel and noticed "Class of 2024" embroidered on the edge. That year was far away, way past my prognosis. I wandered away from the group of moms to watch Kalea play basketball with a few boys. Would she still play basketball in high school? I pictured her in a cap and gown, her long hair in curls hitting her shoulders. Would I still be here, or would she look out into the crowd to an empty chair? Those thoughts caught me sometimes by surprise, crushing my soul.

"Mom! That was the best night ever!" she said as she wrapped her arms around me. I hugged her back, but she pulled away to say goodbye to her friends. That was one of the hardest things. She was at an age where she was growing away from me, while I was trying desperately to hold on.

* *

On the way to the marriage conference, Mike didn't say much. I was excited when a lovely couple from church gifted us the weekend getaway, but Mike didn't want to discuss his feelings in front of strangers. It wasn't that kind of format, but he didn't believe me. He didn't think we needed it, but we did. We were drifting apart again and this time away would be good for us. I wanted us to reconnect and I prayed God would touch his heart.

We walked into the conference center and signed in at the registration table. The enthusiastic greeters immediately gave us name tags and a Sharpie. I didn't look at Mike. I knew it would spark a sarcastic comment. He was a good sport as he proudly slapped his name tag on his chest. We picked up our workbooks and pens and went into the ballroom. Mike walked straight to the very last row. Just like in church or any event, he preferred the back. I was a front row girl, but followed his lead.

"Where do you want to go for date night?" he asked. The conference wrapped up at four on Saturday so couples could go on a date. Some couples made elaborate plans. We hadn't even discussed it.

The first speaker took the stage. I sat up in my chair, and Mike sat back like he was settling in for a nap on a really long flight. The first session felt like a comedy show. We both laughed so hard as the speaker talked about communication in a marriage.

"When your wife or husband tells a story, does it include about a dozen back stories before it gets started?"

Mike elbowed me as he smiled and looked straight ahead.

"Couples usually have different communication styles that lead to misunderstanding." the speaker continued. We completed an exercise and compared our answers. We were exact opposites in our communication styles. I noticed Mike sat up in his chair, actively listening.

At the end of the session, the speaker asked participants to accept Christ into their hearts. For those who had not done so, or who wanted to reaffirm their faith, he asked them to join him in prayer. There was a box in our workbook to check if you chose to do so.

Mike was a believer, but he questioned his faith when I was diagnosed again. I glanced at his paper as we closed the session. The box was not checked. It didn't mean he didn't believe, but I hoped to see a checkmark in that box.

"This was totally different than I expected," Mike said as we left the ballroom. "I thought we were going to sit in a big circle, answering questions about our marriages. Kumbaya kind of stuff."

"You didn't trust me?" I asked.

"I had to see it to believe it," Mike said laughing.

The next day we sat through several sessions, each one providing more insight into marriage. The speakers were funny and engaging, the exercises eye-opening.

"I feel disrespected when it comes to the kids," he admitted during one of our breakout sessions. "I usually agree with you, but it would be nice to be included in decisions. Run things by me, or tell me what is going on with them."

When the kids were little and he traveled so much, I had to do things by myself. I didn't intentionally leave him out. I was used to handling them on my own. I was pretty independent. He was right. I didn't always include him. I had no idea he felt that way.

"I can do that," I said. "I'm sorry. I just handle things. I never meant to be disrespectful."

"You don't have to go crazy, just fill me in once in a while." That was an easy fix.

We both wanted to spend more time together away from the kids.

"I want date nights. Not just every few months," I told him. "Maybe we can't fit it in weekly, but at least monthly."

"No," Mike disagreed. "We can fit it in weekly. We just don't."

"You're right," I said. "We don't have to plan fancy dinners all the time. We can have lunch dates in the week. We can go for a walk in the evening. We just need to make time for each other."

We both enjoyed family time, but Mike felt I devoted all my energy to the kids.

"Sometimes, you ignore me because the kids need you for something." I looked at him defensively. He was a grown man.

"Hear me out. I know the kids need you, but they are getting older. They can do more on their own. If we are having a conversation and the kids walk in the room, why do we have to drop what we are doing to help Kade find his game or Kalea look for her shoes?"

"You're right!" I agreed. "We don't." I could think back to about a dozen examples in just the last few days. Conversations never finished. Discussions interrupted.

"They have to respect our relationship, too. We just listened to them talk about that," Mike said, recalling the session about putting our relationship first, as God intended.

At the end of Saturday's session, we went back to our hotel room to get ready for our date. I felt closer to him already. We really were on the same page about most things, but needed to better prioritize our relationship. And, of course, we learned communication was key!

Getting ready to go out felt like old times. We were Mike and Jen, not Kalea and Kade's parents. We went to dinner at a fun meatball joint, and it felt like we were dating again. We promised not to talk about the kids, but the conversation naturally came around to them. We quickly changed the subject. As the lines of communication opened, we inevitably got around to the elephant in the room.

Cancer.

"I guess I never imagined life turning out this way. I thought we were going to be old and gray and retire near the beach somewhere. I never thought this would happen," he admitted. "It kills me to think about it."

All those times when he didn't want to talk about it, I worried he was in denial or worse, wasn't affected by it at all. He shared with me all the pain he felt over the last few years. He made me understand what he went through as my husband. It opened up my eyes. I thanked God I was the sick one. I would take it a hundred times to keep my husband or my kids from going through this. I never saw how much he was hurting. It broke my heart. I needed to show him more compassion instead of being so defensive. Cancer happened to both of us. Mike told me that once.

When we arrived at the Sunday morning session, I was sad the conference was almost over. Husbands and wives were separated for the morning session. Mike kissed me goodbye and I watched him walk away to the other room, sad to see him go.

The female speaker took the stage. I was convicted by some of her statements. Mike traveled a lot for work, especially when the kids were younger. I was left at home working full-time building a business and taking care of the kids. I struggled through dinner, bath time, and bedtime on my own while he ate at a restaurant or ordered food and enjoyed a quiet night in a hotel room. What I wouldn't have given for one night like that? When he came home, he complained about how tired he was. I used to get so angry. He was tired? I was cold and defensive and never considered that he worked hard too.

"Women worked hard whether they worked in the home or outside of it," she said. "When spouses kept score, marriage turned into competition. When marriage became a competition, there was no winner, only two losers."

Yes, we were both driven people. Mike was more competitive than me, but I did keep score. There were times in our marriage when we were definitely two losers.

The stories she shared convicted me. I definitely had some work to do. The speaker gave me so many nuggets of wisdom. I wanted to implement everything I learned. When Mike returned, he gave me a big hug. I could tell his time was as enlightening as mine.

During the final session, the speaker who was also a minister, asked everyone to stand and face their spouses. He led us in a vow renewal service. Although over a hundred couples stood beside us, it felt like we were the only ones in the room. Through tears, Mike and I repeated the vows we said years ago, but they meant so much more that day.

"I now pronounce you husband and wife. You may kiss your bride."

And that was that. We were married. Again.

At the close of the session, the speaker once again said a prayer, asking for those who were willing to accept Jesus into their hearts to join him. We all prayed together. He asked those who recommitted their lives to Christ to please check the box on the handout. As Mike gathered his things, I sorted the handouts from the feedback forms. That's when I saw it. A checkmark. I smiled to myself, looked up, and thanked God.

Mike had been so angry. He questioned his faith when I got sick. I worried about his salvation. I wanted Mike to rely on God when things turned a corner for me. I wanted my children to continue to go to church when I was gone. This meant everything to me. Mike and I grew closer that weekend. We said things we never said to each other. We renewed our vows. But this! This was the best thing that happened that weekend. Praise the Lord for answered prayers.

* *

The morning light was just breaking through as I sat at the morning room table. Everyone was still asleep. Sipping my chamomile tea, I leaned back against the chair. The sun sprinkled its rays through the trees. Birds fluttered from branch to branch. A bunny hopped slowly through the back yard until it bolted down the hill in a blur. I listened to the hum of the refrigerator and the birds chirping outside.

It was summertime. I put away the backpacks and lunchboxes and forgot the morning routine. It was my first summer with the kids after I stopped working. I planned to spend our days at the pool or at the park. Sit outside in the evenings and watch them play with the neighbor kids. No homework. No school projects.

I was writing again. Reading so many books. It had been so long since I had time to read. Mike and I made date night a priority. We ate dinner as a family at the table. I planned many lunch dates with friends. I was learning to navigate this 'life with cancer' thing. A quiet rain suddenly began to fall. I listened to the raindrops hit the window. I loved the sound of rain. I took another sip of tea. One day my scans would show progression. One day, life would take another hard left. Not today. As I traveled down this road of "in between", I planned to enjoy the ride.

Chapter Thirty-Five

My insurance company denied my scan. I called Lori at the cancer center.
"You have had 4 petscans since you started Ibrance. They only allow for 4 during any one treatment. Since you had 4 while on Ibrance, they won't pay for another one."
"Ever?" I asked, confused.
"Nope," explained Lori. "Not until you change treatment. With your diagnosis, they think you won't need more than 4."
"So, you mean they expected I'd be dead by now?" I asked.
"Pretty much."

I had an appointment with Dr. Mendez. I would have to tell him about my leg. The pain had been off and on for a couple of months now. It was deep in my thigh bone and reminded me of the pain in my elbow. I knew he'd schedule a scan. We were trying to wait six months instead of three, but I couldn't wait that long.

I sat in the exam room long enough for the lights to turn off. I didn't feel like getting up to trigger the motion sensor. I rested my head against the wall until I heard Dr. Mendez' footsteps and familiar knock.

"Look at you, sitting in the dark," Dr. Mendez said, flipping on the light. Then he apologized for the wait. I never minded waiting for him.

I told him about my leg, knowing what he was going to say.

"You know I have to send you for a scan. Let's see what is going on there," Dr. Mendez said. He seemed concerned. He usually told me that it could be anything and not to worry, but he didn't say that this time. My tumor markers had been creeping up. It wasn't much, but enough to make me a little nervous.

The nurse scheduled the scan with the hospital for the following week. Susan and Chrissie picked me up very early in the morning. We laughed the whole way to the hospital.

"Where are we going to eat?" asked Susan. "I think we should try that new place in Carnegie." Always the foodie, Susan pulled up the menu on her phone. I wasn't interested in food,but I played along.

We found a waiting room and I went to the registration area. Randy was there again. We chatted while we waited for the IV team. I heard Susan and Chrissie laughing down the hall. Randy looked in that direction, probably wondering why people were so loud so early in the morning.

"They're with me," I told him. He laughed and told me some crazy patient stories until the IV nurse came in with supplies.

"You called for the IV team," she said. She was all business, not a hint of a smile. Randy jumped up and walked into the hallway. She looked at my arm and scowled. After a couple of failed attempts, she wrapped my arm in a warm towel and walked away in a huff. I felt the tears roll down my cheeks.

Noticing the commotion in my room, Chrissie asked the nurse if they could come back with me. She said they could stand in the hall but could not enter the room.

"Hey there!" Chrissie said, as they peeked in the door and stepped back against the wall in the hallway.

"They can't find my vein," I said, explaining what was going on. I started to cry.

"It's okay. They are professionals. They will get the job done," Chrissie said trying to reassure me.

"They have to hurry this up," Susan said. "I'm starving!"

We all laughed. I could always count on Susan to joke during a stressful time.

A few moments later, the cranky nurse returned. Susan and Chrissie made funny faces behind her back and walked away. I didn't want to laugh at the lady with the needle. I heard Susan and Chrissie whisper and then erupt into more laughter.

I loved those ladies.

The cranky nurse found a vein and I got my injection. When my hour was up, Randy walked me to the scan room. Being in that tube made me anxious. I said a prayer and went to my happy place. It was January 2005 and I was in Oahu on Waikiki Beach, looking up at a palm tree and listening to the ocean.

I lost my father the year before and was still grieving. We had been trying to get pregnant. Month after month, I bought a test. It was always negative. We made an appointment at a fertility clinic but couldn't be seen until April. We decided to stop stressing. No more temperatures. No more calendars. We would wait until April and see what the doctor said.

I listened to the ocean waves, the bits of conversations of passers-by and the Hawaiian music that seemed to play continuously around the island. I let the water carry away all the grief and sadness in my heart. The island soothed my soul. That trip was such a blessing. Hawaii was a true paradise, the closest place to heaven I could imagine. I took a mental picture of the view from under the palm tree. That picture was my happy place ever since.

"All done," I heard Randy say as the whirring of the machine slowed and stopped. I didn't want to come back from under that palm tree.

The weekend before my fertility appointment, we helped Mom clean out the basement. We went through Dad's things. We found his coal mine safety training materials from his early career. We found boxes of silver and stones, stacks of glass, and supplies from his many hobbies. Going through Dad's things was emotional. It was like sifting through all those little pieces of his life that made him whole.

On the way home, I stopped to buy a pregnancy test. I was a couple of days late. I almost didn't bother because it was always a disappointment. I couldn't believe it when I picked up the test and saw two lines. It was positive! I ran downstairs to show Mike.

"We are going to have a baby!" he said, jumping up from his chair. We were finally pregnant. We waited so long. The next day, I called to cancel my appointment. It was in a few days.

"You would be surprised how often that happens, honey. Sometimes all it takes is to stop trying so hard. Stop the worrying and let things go. I am so happy for you," said the receptionist. "God bless you."

She was so right. It wasn't until we stopped all the temperature monitoring, analyzing, and test taking that we finally got pregnant. Hawaii was our big exhale. We let go of all the stress and sadness of the last year. It was a testimony of faith. Only when we truly casted our cares on God and put our faith in Him did we find peace. With that peace came happiness. We welcomed our daughter into the world that December. Kalea was a Hawaiian name. A few months later, I was pregnant with Kade. The kids were only 10 ½ months apart. Within one year we became a family of four. Our family was complete.

"Your doctor should have these results by the end of the day," Randy said. "Go get some breakfast with your friends."

We had breakfast at the new restaurant Susan mentioned. I ordered chocolate chip pancakes and bacon. We all laughed and carried on as usual. They dropped me off at home later that morning and all I could do was wait.

I was nervous this time. Something was definitely going on with my femur. This all felt so familiar. Dr. Mendez didn't call that afternoon. The last time he called me right away. When I got the stage 4 diagnosis, he waited to tell me in person.

"He didn't call," I said to Mike. "It must be bad news."

"Don't say that," Mike said, trying to calm me down. "He is busy. Maybe he didn't get the results yet. He will call."

"I am going to go upstairs for a little while. You have the kids?" I asked. Mike nodded. I needed to be alone. I got a hot shower and collapsed in a heap on the bed. The waiting was hard.

I wanted more birthdays and holidays. More ordinary days. I knew my hourglass was no longer top-heavy and the end of the ball was near, but I had so much more dancing to do.

I thought of all the dresses and ties, the Christmas presents, and the birthday cakes. I wondered if Mike would go too long without eating, get enough sleep. Would my *Mom Squad* sit comfortably in a booth for two? Would Mom bake her apricot cookies at Christmastime? My mind scrolled through snapshots of family events going on without me. Grief gripped me from the inside out. One microscopic cancer cell, one bad scan could change my life forever, and there was nothing I could do about it. If I spent the next 24 hours sobbing on this bed and my scans were clear, I wasted a perfectly good day. If my scans were bad, I wasted my last good 24 hours. I had to focus on right now, this very moment. The in between was all I had.

I washed my face and went downstairs. Kalea was drawing a picture, Kade was looking at a book, and Mike was watching television.

"Movie night, anyone?" I asked.

"Yay!" Kalea screamed, putting the cap on her marker. "Can we have popcorn and candy?"

"I'll get the pillows and blankets," yelled Kade, throwing pillows from the couch onto the floor.

"Yes, and yes!" I agreed, pulling the popcorn from the pantry.

We snuggled on the floor in a mountain of pillows and blankets. When the movie was over, there were popcorn crumbs all over the floor and Kade had Skittles stuck to the bottom of his pajamas. It was a mess, but it was the perfect night.

The next morning, after the kids went off to school. Mike and I were in the living room when Dr. Mendez called.

"Jen, your scans look great! I have to admit I was sick all weekend worrying that this was going to be the one. I didn't want to call you with bad news. I am so pleased your cancer is stable. The pain in your leg is probably arthritis brought on by medical menopause and your medications."

I thanked Dr. Mendez. Mike and I sat quietly for a moment.

"I was scared," I broke the silence. "I even practiced what I was going to say to the kids."

"I know," said Mike, with a big exhale. "Now I can work again. And sleep. And eat."

"What?" I asked. As usual, Mike seemed pretty calm over the weekend.

"I was a wreck. I was behind on work. I went into my office and couldn't think. I couldn't eat. My stomach was a mess. I couldn't sleep. I stared at the ceiling all night."

"Really? I didn't know."

"Well, I couldn't tell you that."

* *

We were on our way home from the grocery store when Mike's phone rang. I saw Mike's face and knew. Chuck was gone.

Mike's oldest brother had stage four liver cancer. We knew this call was coming. My heart broke for Mike as he tried to hold back his tears. I wanted to tell him he didn't have to be strong. Not with me. I took his hand and we sat in silence the rest of the way home. I didn't have the words.

Chuck was there the night I met Mike. He said he knew back then we were meant to be. Many times, Chuck pulled me aside to thank me for being a good wife to his brother. His words meant so much. Chuck and I had some deep conversations. Being able to talk to someone openly about having end-stage cancer was a blessing. We couldn't discuss everything with friends and family. We didn't want to hurt them. We covered tough topics, but our conversations were always positive.

We faced cancer the same way. We wanted quality over quantity, to live in the moment, and to fight until the end. Chuck used to hate the QOL (quality of life) conversation with the doctors.

"You take care of the quantity part, Doc. I'll take care of the rest," he used to say.

Last November, Chuck made the trip from Florida to visit with his mom, Mike, and his brother Gary. We planned an early Thanksgiving dinner, piling around his mom's small kitchen table. Chuck didn't feel much like eating but the boys shared stories and laughs.

After dinner, the others moved to the living room, but Chuck stayed with his mom as she finished a piece of pie. I cleared the table while the two of them laughed about something. Chuck put his arm around his mom. They both closed their eyes for a moment as Chuck rested his head against hers.

"Love you, Ma," Chuck said as they held onto each other. My heart broke for them, for all of them. The boys lost their dad when Mike was in college. Mike's Mom lost her husband, the love of her life, and would soon lose her first-born son. That knowledge made the day more difficult and more special at the same time. Such love and strength gathered around the table.

We all knew that was our last Thanksgiving with Chuck. Mike's mom would never sit around a dinner table with all three boys again, but he was there that night.

"Ride it until the wheels fall off." That was something Chuck always said. That's how I wanted to live my life too. Knowing I was going to die was hard, but empowering. I would one day spend that last holiday with my family too. I wanted to talk and laugh and remember. I wanted to grab my family members and tell them I loved them the way Chuck told his mom at the table that night. I wanted to ride this life until the wheels fell off, just like Chuck.

* *

"Mom, look!" Kalea yelled from the passenger seat, pointing out the window. Up in the sky were ribbons of pink, purple, and orange. It looked like a big scoop of rainbow sherbert.

"Want to go to the lake or to the park?" she asked. She knew the drill. She had been along on many car rides to find the perfect view of an evening sunset.

"Let's do the lake," I decided. "It's closer." I made a quick right hand turn. The sun was about to set and I didn't want to miss it. Kalea watched it like she could keep the sun from setting.

I pulled into the gravel lot and reached for my phone. We jumped out of the car and walked to the water's edge.

"It's so pretty, Mommy," she said as she gazed up at the gorgeous sky. "Look how it reflects on the water."

She was as excited about sunsets as I was. Both my kids pointed out sunsets and sun rays that slipped through the clouds. Mike did too. I told them those rays were windows where our loved ones looked down on us from heaven. Often, Mke sent a picture of a sunset he was traveling or friends sent one on a random night. I felt blessed that my loved ones saw something so beautiful and thought of me.

"God paints us pictures all the time," I told her. "It makes Him happy when we notice."

We watched the kaleidoscope of colors until the sun slipped behind the hills.

"Next time, I hope we get to see it for longer," Kalea said, checking out the pictures she took on the way home. "It's never as good in the picture as it is in real life either."

"Nothing ever is, Sweet Pea."

Chapter Thirty-Six

*After completing a 10-page application to rescue a dog,
the rescue agency replied by email...*

Dear Mrs. Collins,
*We have some concerns about your application. What will
your husband do with the dog when you die? He would be
overwhelmed as a new single parent. We must deny your
application because we fear your husband will give the dog
away after your death.*
Thank you for your interest.

"We are going to Carolina Beach, North Carolina!" I said as the kids jumped up and down. My family was selected for a week's vacation through Little Pink Houses of Hope, an organization that gave families of breast cancer patients an all-expenses paid vacation away from cancer. Last fall, I saw a post about Little Pink. I filled out the application and wrote an essay about my family. Before I hit the submit button, I prayed.

Lord, my family could really use this vacation. If there is a place for us, and if we wouldn't take it from someone else who needed it more, we would love to go. We could use this time as a family. If it is Your Will, then we would be so grateful.

The following February, I received an email that we were selected.

We drove 10 hours to get to Kate's Pancake House in Carolina Beach to meet the volunteers and get the keys to our home for the week. When we walked inside the cozy diner, we were greeted with hugs and cheers. We met our VolunStar, Kathy, who invited us to sit down and relax for a few minutes. I recognized Angi from across the crowded room. We met on the Facebook page Little Pink set up for all the attendees. We lived less than thirty minutes from each other, our kids were around the same age, and we saw the same doctor.

"I'll catch you later at dinner!" Angi yelled and waved. I couldn't wait.

Kathy got in her car and we followed her to our beach house. As we stepped inside, I was overwhelmed. The home was gorgeous. The kids had their own rooms and bathrooms. The master bedroom on the top floor had a walkout porch and an ocean view. After Kathy gave us a tour, she brought us down to the kitchen, already stocked with supplies and our favorite foods. On the kitchen table were bags of beach items like towels, sunscreen, sunglasses, and hats. They thought of everything.

Later that night, we attended a spaghetti dinner provided by the local fire station. We met the volunteers and other families. The women had early stage and metastatic disease. Some had young children and teenagers, adult children, and even grandchildren. Most women were doing well while others were struggling.

The next morning was supposed to be a beach day, but it rained. We spent the morning at a gym so the kids could tumble and play. Mike was on the floor with Kalea, Kade and the rest of the kids. I spent time with Angi. She was a character. Because she wasn't feeling well, she was in a wheelchair. Despite her failing health, she was hilarious. She loved to write, was a woman of faith, and a doting mom. Her husband Tom was a youth softball coach like Mike. Her daughter loved softball and YouTube videos and her son loved karate, video games, and the outdoors. Our families had so much in common. I was instantly drawn to her.

Later in the week, Angi and I discussed plans to get together once we got home. We wanted to see one of her daughter's softball games and maybe go camping. Angi recently transferred to a different doctor.

"Oh my, you have to go see my doctor. At the front desk, they have these amazing lemon balls. These candies are so good," she said, her eyes smiling with excitement. "You should make an appointment just to try those lemon balls!"

"You are too much," I said. I had only known Angi for a short time, but I adored her.

We had a wonderful time that week. I watched the stress visibly drain from my whole family. We hadn't been on a real vacation since the kids were babies. I was too busy with the center and then I got sick. There was no time, and then there was no money.

Mike relaxed. Kalea got away from the pressures of growing up and fitting in. Kade showed more courage than I had seen in a long time. He fished, touched a shark, and even paddle boarded. The volunteers were good to all of us, but they went out of their way to make Kade feel accepted. He needed that. The people involved with Little Pink were amazing.

I reconnected and made memories with my family. I sat on the beach. I spent more than a few minutes with my husband. My family was in the same place at the same time. It was one of the most joyous weeks of my life.

We were so sad to leave Carolina Beach. We stopped to eat breakfast at Kate's Pancake House one more time before we hit the road. We drove away from the beach, that amazing house, and those beautiful people that morning, but we took a little bit of Carolina Beach along with us.

We stopped on the way home to tour a naval ship and took a detour to Charlottesville, Virginia. Mike graduated from the University of Virginia. The kids enjoyed seeing where their dad went to school and listening to the funny stories about his time there. Those unplanned stops were always the best.

"Oh no!" I said, startling Mike on the drive home. Angi wasn't doing well. Tom took her to the hospital as soon as they made it home.

The kids went back to school the following Monday and Mike went back to work. That love and light we felt at Carolina Beach stayed with us though. I watched for updates about Angi, anxious to go visit her when Tom said it was okay. I couldn't wait. I never got to visit Angi though. Two weeks after we left Carolina Beach, Mike and I paid our respects to Tom and the kids at the funeral home. Metastatic breast cancer had stolen another beautiful soul.

Rest in peace, sweet Angi.

Chapter Thirty-Seven

I keep hearing about how sick you are, cancer and everything,"
said a man I hadn't seen in a while. "How are you doing?"
"I'm doing well, My last scans were stable," I said. He looked
at me, a confused look on his face.
"Yeah, I don't get it," he said. "You look fine to me."
He walked away.

My birthday was coming up again. I wanted to do something with Mike since I spent my last birthday with my friends. One night, as I sat on the love seat pretending to watch a baseball game with Mike, I got a text from Susan.

"I talked to Mike. He had no plans yet, so me and Chrissie are taking you to dinner for your birthday."

I loved them, but that was not what I planned.

"You told Susan you didn't have any plans for my birthday?"

"I didn't make any plans yet. I didn't know what you wanted to do. I figured you could go with them and we could celebrate on Sunday, on your actual birthday."

"I wanted to go somewhere with you on my birthday," I said, rolling my eyes.

"We can," he said. "On Sunday, your actual birthday."

Ugh. He didn't get it. I wanted to celebrate with him. It felt like he passed me off to my friends. I didn't know how many birthdays I had left. Special days were more important to me now. I hoped Mike would make it up to me by planning something extra special for Sunday.

Chrissie was already in the car when Susan picked me up that night.

"Good thing I took my Dramamine," said Chrissie. "This one's driving makes me sick."

"We got here, didn't we?" protested Susan. "Have I ever not gotten you where we were going safe and sound?"

When we walked in the restaurant, there were plenty of empty tables.

"I'm not sure we needed a reservation," I said, laughing. The hostess grabbed a few menus and headed past the empty tables to a back room. I noticed Lynn first. I saw my friend Kierstin and then Wilma. I scanned the room and saw all my friends.

"Surprise!" Susan said as she directed me to a chair. "Mike is on his way too!" Susan planned everything, but Mike was in on it. He walked in a few minutes later.

"I know you're mad," Mike said in my ear as he hugged me. "I'm sorry. I didn't know what to do. I didn't want to give it away. I am horrible with this stuff."

"It's okay," I said, smiling. "I forgive you."

My friends were a chatty bunch. I looked around the room at all these wonderful women. My circle. They were all so busy, but they took time on a Saturday night in the crazy month of May to celebrate my birthday with me. I sat back in my chair and looked around.

"Taking it all in?" asked Lynn, who was sitting next to me.

"Yes," I said. "I had no idea. I know how busy everyone is this time of year. It means a lot to have you all here." Just then, Susan stood up to get everyone's attention.

"Thank you all for coming. Jen, I sent out a Facebook message and said, 'Raise your hand if your life has been touched by Jen'. Every one of them responded." she explained how she pulled it all together. "We wanted to do something special for you. We love you. Happy Birthday." Her kind words and the love I felt that night helped to lift my spirits after losing Chuck and Angi.

A waitress entered the room carrying a beautiful cake decorated with flowers and lit with candles. I was usually uncomfortable when people sang "Happy Birthday" to me, but tonight I didn't mind. I blew out all the candles. I didn't make a wish. I had everything I needed.

Chapter Thirty-Eight

I walked up to a group of people and introduced myself.
"Oh, you're the girl with cancer, right?"
"Oh, yeah, I heard about you. I'm so sorry."
"So, what's it like? Do you sit around thinking about when
you are going to die?"

"Hi there! I am just checking in on you. How are you doing?" I texted Deena.

"My brain scan results confirmed that every spot got smaller. I have an MRI on my abdomen in a few weeks to see if my liver spots have changed at all," she messaged back.

I never heard back about the MRI results and sent her a message to see how she was doing.

Deena was a friend of Mike's cousin, who asked me to reach out to her when she was diagnosed with metastatic breast cancer. We became fast friends, much like Debbie and me. She was married with a young daughter and was determined to fight this dreadful disease. She was funny and brutally honest. We vented to each other all the time.

"It's funny because people ask how you are and when you do say exactly how you feel, it's almost like they tune you out. I know people are genuinely concerned but they don't understand. Not fully—and they never will," she said, frustrated. "No one understands that we live day to day wondering how many days we have left."

Deena was right. When people asked how I was doing, I usually gave a stock answer.

"I'm doing great. Last scans were stable," or "I'm tired, but doing alright." I didn't like to complain with a random list of side effects. When I answered honestly, the subject was changed or the conversation was dropped. Maybe it hurt too much when they heard it. I couldn't blame them. I probably treated Dad the same way.

Even with all the pain and uncertainty, the worst part was how this affected our children.

"It's really, really scary," Deena said. "I just hope I can find a treatment that works that at least allows me to see my daughter grow up as long as I can. I'm sure, as any death would, it will break her. She is not ready for that right now. I can come to terms with me not living a full life because of this disease and I get that. I accept that this disease could take me at any time. I just need more time with her," she said one night after yet another bad scan.

I understood my life would be shorter than I expected. I was okay with that too. My concern was my children. I wanted more time for them. Deena's condition was much more serious than mine. She did not respond to several different treatments and her doctor tried one drug after another when scans showed progression. It sounded like this current treatment was working. I was anxious to find out the results of her MRI. It often took her days or a couple of weeks to get back to me. She was living her 'in between' as best she could too.

* *

Kade and his friend, Isabella, were outside in the driveway crouched on the ground looking at something when I pulled in the garage. I was almost afraid to find out, but walked over to see. A monarch butterfly with a broken wing stuck on its side on the pavement. Kade said it had been there all day. There wasn't much we could do, but I couldn't leave it out there to die.

After a Google search and a couple of Youtube videos, we constructed a butterfly habitat complete with a stick for perching, some leaves and grass for ambiance, and a cotton ball soaked with sugar water for nourishment. We placed the large glass jar on the morning room table in front of the windows so the butterfly had a view. I took the liberty of naming him Mister Mister.

"What's that mean?" the kids asked.

"If you grew up in the 80's, you wouldn't have to ask," I said, then played them the song.

"Take... these broken wings," the kids sang along, laughing.

"Poor Mister, Mister," said Isabella.

Every day, we soaked cotton balls in a fresh batch of sugar water. Mister Mister adjusted to his new surroundings. He even fluttered several inches off the stick testing out his wings. Through our research, we knew his wing could not be mended, but we were prepared to take care of him for the rest of his life. Sadly, that life was over a week later.

"We gave him a whole week of extra life," Kade said. "And we made that week good for him. He spent his last days being nothing but happy."

"He sure did," I said.

"Yep. We made a difference," said Kade.

"When you have the chance, Bud," I said, "I hope you will always make a difference."

* *

Susan, Chrissie, Stacy, and I saw *Steel Magnolias* at a local theater. It was one of my favorite movies. The live production was a little different but all the characters and the events were the same. We watched Shelby get married. We laughed when Ouiser got mad at Drum. We cried with M'Lynn when Shelby died.

We watched those Southern women support each other through the good times and bad. At the end of the production, we gave the cast a standing ovation. I looked to my left and to my right at the women beside me, three of the strongest women I knew. All had overcome struggles in their lives. We were always there for each other. They stepped up for me and my family, not just when I was sick, but through all the daily struggles life threw at us.

When the kids were in elementary school, we met on that bench at three every afternoon. We discussed the world's problems along with what was on sale at the grocery store. We met for lunch at the Springhouse on good days and often, for ice cream at Sarris on the bad days. Carrying each other's burdens, we showed up at each other's houses with baked goods, groceries, cleaning supplies, or to lend an ear. We had our fair share of squabbles and disagreements and sometimes fought like sisters, but when one of us was in need, we showed up. We have gathered in our homes and in ice cream parlors and sadly, too many funeral homes.

We talked about life and we talked about death. We talked about how Chrissie wanted sale ads instead of flowers at her funeral and how I wanted nothing that resembled a traditional funeral. We talked about what would happen when I was gone. I wanted them to help decorate my house for Christmas for my kids, if Mike just couldn't do it. I wanted them to take Kalea shopping to find the perfect dress for her prom.

They didn't like when I made jokes about who would referee when I was gone. I teased they would have to do math all by themselves one day. They could go to a sushi place for lunch, because I hated sushi. They agreed to make sure people who were unkind to me didn't show up at my funeral. They also promised to watch out for opportunistic women looking to snag themselves a Superman too.

We laughed, but I saw concern on their faces and tears they tried to hide during the scary times. I saw the stolen glances across the table when the conversations turned uncomfortable. They were scared too but didn't show it. Sometimes I felt dismissed when they said things like "It's all going to be fine" and "Don't worry", but they were trying to convince themselves as much as me.

Even when things got hard and my health declined, they would be there. They would bring lunch to my bedside when I could no longer join them elsewhere. They would make me laugh and keep me company when I was too weak to join in the conversation. They would help my family navigate all the sad stuff at the end of my life and stand beside them the day they had to say goodbye. Even when their hearts were broken, they would do what needed to be done.

Mike was my rock, but the women in my life were strong in a different way. Women swallowed down their pain and suffering for the sake of their children and families. They held back tears. They walked through the fire. They told their loved ones it would be okay, even when they knew it wouldn't. They did the same for their friends.

When M'Lynn described sitting with Shelby as she took her last breath, she sat alone. Shelby's father and husband couldn't watch. But M'Lynn stayed. She stayed until the end. Then, she said something that resonated with me forever...

"I find it amusing. Men are supposed to be made out of steel or something."

I joked about dying, more often than I should. It was a coping mechanism, maybe. Or a really dark sense of humor. I wasn't afraid of dying, but I was terrified of leaving my family. I knew they would be okay, though. God provided for me a beautiful bouquet of steel magnolias.

Chapter Thirty Nine

Talking to an old high school friend who is a health coach...
"You don't eat sugar, do you? That feeds the cancer!"
Me: "...No" (moves phone from mouth to take a bite
of my cookie)

I took one last look around. Every Christmas, I forgot something. A set of holiday candlesticks was on the library table. Almost missed them. Packing up holiday decorations was emotional. I feared I was celebrating my last one. I wanted to enjoy the holidays, but those thoughts stole my joy. I put pressure on myself to orchestrate the best holiday, creating lasting memories and instilling a sense of tradition in my kids. I had to do all the things.

It took a while but I learned to let go of the vision in my head, that one straight out of a movie. House meticulously decorated. Matching Christmas pajamas. Holiday feasts. I struggled to pick out the perfect presents. My expectations were way too high. Thankfully, I got through the holiday season better than I used to, but packing up after the holidays still got to me. Every year, I intended to write a note to Mike and the kids and stick it in their stockings. Just in case. I could never bring myself to do it. As I closed the lid on the last bin, I prayed.

Thank you for this holiday season. I am grateful for another Christmas spent with my family. Please bless us in the year to come. I ask for your protection over all of us. May the year be filled with health and happiness and may we seek to grow closer to you every day. I pray I will be here to open these bins and hang these decorations next year. If that is not Your Will, I pray the memories will comfort them, and my family will still feel joy and the Christmas Spirit in their hearts.

I stacked the bins near the door so Mike could return them to the loft in the garage.

Until next year, I hope.

* *

"What do you want to say?" I asked. I sat down next to Kade at the dining room table. He asked me to help him write his testimony for his baptism service the following week.

"I need to talk about when I became a believer, how God works in my life, and choose a favorite verse," he said, showing me his notebook from baptism class.

I was so excited Kade chose to be baptized when our youth pastor asked the youth group. He went to classes on Saturdays with his friend Isabella and the other kids. The following Sunday, Kade would be baptized in front of our church and would read his testimony during the ceremony. He was really nervous about that part.

I asked him questions, but wanted his testimony to be in his own words. He told me how he accepted Jesus into his heart when he attended Vacation Bible School. He wrote that down in his notebook.

"How does God work in your life, Bud?" I asked. His eyes darted around the room as he thought about the question. He was a deep-thinker so I sat quietly, giving him time to respond.

"I pray a lot. I pray to God when I need Him. I am nervous before my karate tests and when I have to speak in front of people. He brings me peace and gives me courage," he said.

"See. That's perfect," I said, and watched him carefully write those thoughts down on paper. With a serious expression on his face, he looked so grown up. He was a twelve-year-old boy with an old soul.

"As you know," Kade continued matter-of-factly, without making eye contact. "I am very shy. I feel unsure about myself sometimes. I pray about that too."

"Do you pray for God to make you less shy?" I asked. I didn't want to make him uncomfortable, but I was curious since he was being so open.

"Not really. Well? Maybe sometimes," he said. "God tells me I'm special. He made me that way." Kade never looked at me, just continued to write. I sat with him as he finished and had to wipe away a few tears. Kade was painfully shy. I worried about him so much, and was relieved he didn't think something was wrong with him for being so quiet. Knowing he turned to God when he needed help meant the world to me. *Thank you, Lord for watching over my little boy.*

The next Sunday, in front of the whole congregation, Kade was baptized along with his friend Isabella. Despite his nervousness, he shared his heartfelt testimony with confidence and conviction. I was so very proud of him and I knew he was proud of himself. I didn't know how much time I had on this earth. I did my best to teach my children about God and to model a life of faith. I wondered if it was getting through. I didn't have to wonder anymore.

* *

"I'll take Kalea home," I said to Mike. "You guys can stop and pick up milkshakes."

Kalea climbed in the front seat, throwing her muddy cleats on the floor and fastening her seat belt in a huff.

"Come on, Sweet Pea. You played well tonight. You all did," I said, trying to make her feel better. Their team had a tough loss, losing by two in the last inning.

"No we didn't. We all sucked. We couldn't hit. We dropped the ball. The whole team acted like they didn't care," Kalea said, fighting to peel off her sweaty softball sock.

"You did your best. It didn't matter who won in the end," I said.

"Ugh. Enough of the 'feel-good Mom quotes'," she said, still struggling with the sock. "I am getting too old for that stuff. We didn't play well. At all. It's okay to say that."

"Feel-good Mom quotes?"

She pulled the second sock so hard, her knee hit the window when her foot broke free.

"UGH! Stupid sock!" She threw it on the ground and rubbed her knee.

"What a strong sock that was, holding on so tightly to the end," I said. "Good job, sock!"

"Mom!" she said, looking at me like I was crazy. We both started laughing.

"You and your sock both did a good job, Sweet Pea," I said. "I'm always going to try to make you feel better. You are going to have to listen to those 'feel-good Mom quotes' no matter how old you get."

Kalea turned to look out the window. I wanted to always be there to make things better. No one could do that like your Mom. It hurt my heart that one day I wouldn't be there to tell her it was going to be okay. I planned to fill my baby girl's heart with so many "feel-good Mom quotes", she would remember and be encouraged by them even when I was gone.

Chapter Forty

"The price of anything is the amount of life you exchange for it."

HENRY DAVID THOREAU

I know it's hard, Jen, "Dr. Sonja, Dr. Mendez' assistant, said. handing me a tissue. My tears surprised me. Dr. Sonja was always so kind. I saw her and Dr. Mendez on alternating months.

"I just never know if this pain is nothing, or something," I said. "I see women die every day on my cancer pages. These women are living their lives and then, boom! Bad scan. Things decline so fast. They are doing well and then they are gone. It terrifies me."

"Which therapist do you see?" she asked, flipping through my file.

"I don't see a therapist," I said.

"Jen, maybe it would help to talk to someone. Most of our stage 4 patients see a therapist," she said. "I never realized you didn't. Stable or not, you have a serious illness. You are dealing with a lot of emotional stuff. You don't have to talk about cancer. We all have stuff going on."

Dr. Sonja gave me a referral for a therapist who specialized in oncology. I called the next day and set up an appointment. It was hard to talk to loved ones about cancer and dying. My emotions had been all over the place lately. This was going to be good for me.

During one of my first sessions with LeAnn, we talked about being busy and overwhelmed. My calendar was full. I tried to free up my schedule, but always fell back into my old ways. I always felt like I was treading water.

"Do you stay busy to avoid dealing with your emotions. Fear, maybe?"

Maybe. I was strong, but scared too. I was afraid of many things. New pains and progression. Failing. Letting people down. Leaving my family. Friends walking away. Being forgotten. Dying.

I continued to see LeAnn. She taught me to be honest with myself, face my fears, and deal with them. I had to learn to give myself grace. There was no instructional manual on how to deal with this. I never had terminal cancer before. I never nominated myself as the role model for dealing with it. I didn't have to be okay all the time. That was good. Because I wasn't.

* *

I measured the flour and dumped it in the bowl. The mixer hesitated as the batter thickened, but it all came together. I dumped in the chocolate chips. I scooped the batter onto the pans and put them in the oven. They came out perfect.

I made that recipe the day I found out I had cancer, and I made those cookies every August 31st since. Every batch was a statement of love and determination; a reminder of all I had been through. All I overcame. Mixing all those ingredients was affirmation of the promises I made to myself that day. So many changes I made in my life. Those cookies were made with love and I wanted to share them. The best way to defy cancer was to spread as much love and kindness as possible. I planned to bless friends and neighbors later with some chocolate chip cookies. When I was feeling anxious, overwhelmed, or sad, it always made me feel better to do something for someone else.

When life handed me a cancer diagnosis, I turned it into a batch of chocolate chip cookies.

* *

I put the last bag of groceries in the car when I got the message.

"Jen, I wanted to let you know...Deena passed away last night..."

Tears came first, then sobs. No! Not again! Not Deena!

It was too much. I was tired of losing my friends. I was tired of watching families devastated by this disease. I thought about Debbie and Angi and Melanie. Then Terri, and Ellen and Cathy. Crystal and Laura, and Suellen.

There were more. Why couldn't I remember their names? There were so many that I lost count. Every day I saw a post about someone dying from this disease. I couldn't escape it. All those children left behind without the one person who loved them the most in this world. Husbands left to raise children on their own. Although they promised to love until death parted them, they didn't know death would come so soon. They tucked in their children or packed their lunches, knowing they would never do it as well as she did.

I collapsed on the steering wheel. The front of my shirt was soaking wet, my hair stuck to the sides of my face. I reached into the glove compartment and grabbed a stack of fast food napkins to clean my face. I had to drive home. I had to go home to my kids.

I made it through the evening and went to bed early. I had a headache. I didn't dare tell Mike about Deena. Saying it out loud would trigger another breakdown and upset Mike. I curled in a ball on my bed, but I was out of tears. The faces of all the friends I lost circled in my mind. I prayed for their families, and then I prayed for the rest of us living with this cruel disease. Emotionally exhausted, I fell asleep.

I woke up early in the morning. I put on shorts and a sweatshirt and went downstairs. I was going to make a cup of tea but changed my mind. Lacing my shoes tightly with a double knot, I grabbed my phone and my ear buds and went outside. Just before dawn, it was still dark, but the early morning light turned the sky a deep blue. I put the earbuds in, turned up the volume, then hit shuffle on my playlist.

And then I walked.

I walked for Deena and Laura and Melanie. I walked for Ellen and Terri and Angi. I walked for all of them. They couldn't walk anymore, but I could.

My steps were wobbly at first, my feet aching from the neuropathy; my bones and joints protesting the sudden movement. Soon, my feet found their rhythm. *One, Two. One, Two.* I walked hard and I walked fast. Guilt and grief pursued me, but I wasn't going to let them catch me.

As the sun edged over the hillside, its rays caught the dew on the blades of grass and made them sparkle like tiny golden diamonds. The birds chirped in the trees. The sky turned rose–gold, then bronze, then orange like fire.

I kept walking.

A brilliant blue seeped over the heavens and white–puffy–clouds took their places. The sun warmed my face and a gentle breeze cooled my hot skin. My feet hurt, but I kept walking.

My heart pumped blood through my veins and my lungs drew breath. My legs carried my body up the hills and around the corners. I questioned why I was still here and they weren't, but my story wasn't over yet. My steps were numbered but I kept going.

Soon, my muscles were spent, but my soul was renewed. I walked toward home. My steps slowed as the sun warmed my face. I thanked God for today. I thanked God for every day. I didn't know why they were gone, but I was still here.

Yes, I was dying, but not today.

Chapter Forty-One

After explaining to a woman in a waiting room I had
chemotherapy and lost my hair...
Woman: "So that's a wig?"
Me: "Yes."
Woman: "So you have no hair...at all?"
Me: "No."
Woman: "Can I see your bald head?"
Me: "No."

"Come on in," I said, motioning toward the kitchen. Two more ladies carrying pans of brownies were standing at my door. "Everyone is right through there."

My women's Bible study group was making s'mores brownies for Sweet Sunday, a charity event benefiting City Mission. We volunteered every year to make a dessert to raise funds for the wonderful organization. We all made a few batches of brownies and met at my house to cut and prepare them to be sold. I loved hosting events like this, and I loved spending time with these women. I gave up my business and with it, that feeling of working with a team. This group met at the church to study God's Word. I learned so much spiritually, but this group also functioned as a social group, a support group of sorts, and a social service organization. It was amazing. It filled a void in my life. I always looked forward to Wednesday evenings.

That night, more than a dozen ladies worked together, cutting and placing marshmallow, chocolate, and graham cracker covered brownies into cupcake liners. We poured our love into the brownies and into each other. There was laughter, and maybe a few tears, as we visited with each other and came together for a great cause. We fell into a rhythm, working as one body to complete the task. The hands and feet of Christ. At the end of the night, we had over a thousand s'mores brownies ready for the event. It was messy and sticky, but we had fun.

When I joined this group, I was intimidated by these women. They were strong and wise and seemed to have it all together. Their Bibles were full of underlined passages and notes scribbled along the margins. I didn't think I fit in, but they welcomed me with open arms. I learned so much from them. I was still pretty new to the group when I was diagnosed with MBC, but they treated me like family. They delivered meals, and sent encouraging notes and cards. These women carried me through some dark and scary times.

I spent a lifetime trying to prove I could do it all by myself. I never asked for help, even when I so desperately needed it. I was too proud. Maybe too stubborn. These women taught me how to lean into the Lord and how to draw strength from others. Sharing my burdens wasn't a sign of weakness. They never judged, belittled, or criticized. They held me up. They encouraged me. They were some of the most faithful women I knew. I was blessed to be a part of their circle. They taught me I didn't have to do it alone.

* *

For the last two months, my tumor markers steadily increased. Not by much, but enough to have me concerned. I had been really tired and had more aches and pains. Dr. Mendez scheduled a scan to make sure everything was well.

Susan and Chrissie drove me to the hospital. This time, we ended up in another waiting room. Randy was there. He got the IV in the first try and then injected the tracer. I had an hour to sit in that recliner before the test.

"Can my friends come back to that waiting room down the hall?" I asked, grabbing my phone to text them.

"Uh," Randy said, "No, they have to stay where they are. I got in trouble last time."

"Why?" I asked. Randy started to say the waiting room was meant for certain patients.

"My friends were too loud, weren't they?" I interrupted.

"Yeah," Randy said, smiling. "I'm sorry."

I laughed and immediately texted Chrissie and Susan.

"You have to stay where you are. Lol. You caused too much of a disturbance last time. The hospital changed their rules because of you!"

A few moments later, my phone beeped.

"BAHAHAHA!" they responded. They thought it was hilarious.

The pet scan went well. Because my scan was on a Friday, I had to wait through the weekend for the results. By now, I learned to keep enjoying my life. Worrying wouldn't change my results anyway. How many days I wasted when this first started.

We had a fun family weekend. We spent time outside with the kids. Mike helped Kalea practice pitching since softball season was in full swing. We went to Ohiopyle on Saturday and then relaxed on Sunday. I made a big family dinner. When the fear washed over me, I jumped into whatever was going on at the time. My family was my focus for the weekend, not my scans.

On Monday morning, Dr. Mendez called to say my scans looked great. I took a big deep breath, told Mike and my friends the good news, and went to a coffee shop to write. These scans never got easy, but I learned to navigate the waiting and the emotions.

Just another day living with metastatic breast cancer.

* *

I searched online for a local dialysis center. We wanted to treat the staff to lunch in honor of my dad. Since that first birthday after his passing, we did something to bless others in his memory every year on May 13th.

When we arrived, the receptionist showed us to the break room. We decorated the tables and set up the food. I brought a picture of Dad along with some information about him.

"Oh my, this is lovely!" said the receptionist when she popped in to check on us. "They will appreciate this. How long was your dad on dialysis?"

"Seven years," I answered as I placed bowls of Hershey kisses around the tables. "Every Monday, Wednesday, and Friday. He gave the nurses a hard time as only he could, but he loved them. He was grateful to them. So were we."

"Well, thank you ladies," she said as she picked up the picture of my dad and put it on the bulletin board. Dad was smiling down at us. I couldn't hear his laugh or listen to one of his stories again, but I could continue to spread the joy he did when he was on this earth.

That night after dinner, we released balloons up to heaven for Dad's birthday. We stood in the sunshine and watched them drift off into the sky until they disappeared. Dad never got to meet the kids. I shared stories to keep his memory alive. I missed my dad every day, but I drew strength from his example and joy from his memory. I never wanted Dad to just be a picture on a wall to my kids. I wanted them to know him.

"Can we get those scratch off tickets like Grandpap liked?" Kade asked.

"Didn't Grandpap like spicy stuff like me?" Kalea asked a few times.

I loved how he was on their minds like that. I wouldn't get the chance to meet my grandchildren. I hoped that my kids would do the same for me.

Chapter Forty Two

"Owning your story is the bravest thing you will ever do."
BRENE BROWN

I found a table in the corner and set up my laptop. I sat down and stared at a blank screen. I always wanted to write a book, but I never believed I could. Something Susan said all the time stuck in my head lately.

"Jen, God doesn't call the 'equipped'. He equips the 'called'."

I was supposed to write a book. God called me to write it. A few years earlier, Giuseppe told Susan God put on his heart someone was supposed to write a book. He asked Susan if it was her. It wasn't. That evening, Heidi suggested I write a book about living with cancer. She thought it might help people. I texted Susan about it. She told me about Giuseppe. What others may have considered a coincidence, we considered a message received. I was supposed to write a book, and I had to stop making excuses.

"You can do this, Jen," I said to myself. Determined, I sat in that booth, pouring my heart out until a chapter was completed. It felt good.

"Hey there," said Susan, standing over me. "Can I join you for lunch?"

"Sure!," I said, excited to tell her what I was doing.

"I was nearby and thought I would pop in," she said. I put my laptop aside to eat.

Soon, the conversation turned to kids and school and life. Susan's phone rang and she answered the call. I read over my first chapter and heard my phone ring. It was Dr. Mendez' office.

"Hi, Jen," said Julie. "We got your tumor markers back today, and we are concerned. They doubled. We need you to come in right away for a second blood draw. They used a different lab. Maybe that caused the sudden jump."

My tumor markers had been increasing, but by a small amount. They doubled? That never happened before. A different lab shouldn't cause that big of a change.

"I can come right now. We are leaving for the beach in the morning," I said.

"What's wrong?" Susan asked. I told her what was going on as I threw my laptop and notebook in my bag.

"Let's pray right now," Susan said. She bowed her head and prayed for me.

"Amen," we said. I hugged Susan, picked up my bag, and left the coffee shop.

As I drove to the lab, I prepared myself. A big increase in tumor markers usually meant progression. Progression meant my medicine was no longer working and cancer was growing inside me again invading bone, organ, or tissue. I would have to have "that" discussion with my children. This could be the beginning of the end. I pushed the number five in the elevator to the cancer center. I walked through those doors like I had done a hundred times before, but this time it felt very different.

The lab technicians looked at me with pitiful eyes. They watched this scenario play out countless times. Their words of encouragement, though well-intended, brought my emotions to the surface. Two nurses handed me tissues at the same time.

They found a vein on the first attempt. I watched my blood flow through the tiny tube and collect in the vial. I prayed for a different outcome this time as she placed the labels on the tubes and turned to take them away.

"I will call right now and rush these results," the technician said, stopping in the doorway. "I should have them by midday tomorrow." We would be on our way to Ocean City.

The technicians hugged me and I left in tears, terrified.

"My nurse called," I blurted out to Mike when I got home, breaking down in sobs.

"What's wrong?" Mike asked, sitting next to me at the kitchen counter.

When I told him my tumor markers doubled, his eyes grew wide and fear washed over him. He put his elbows on the counter and dropped his face into his hands for a moment. He drew in a breath and looked up at the ceiling. I could barely look at him as I felt his emotions.

The rest of the night was a blur. I texted my friends and asked my prayer warriors to pray for me. I packed snacks for the trip and noticed the calendar. Those white spaces would fill with doctor appointments and scans in the upcoming weeks.

"We've got to go to bed," Mike said, knowing I wouldn't go unless he insisted.

We both stared at the ceiling, restless, knowing tomorrow would bring the news that could change our lives forever.

"We have to have a good time this weekend," I told him. "No matter what."

Mike didn't speak but he pressed his lips together and looked away.

"Before things change," I said. He knew what I meant.

I turned over and pulled the covers tightly around me. I closed my eyes and prayed to God.

Lord, You have given me all this extra time. I have been blessed with years, not months. My kids are 12 and 13. They were 5 and 6 when this all started. Lord, you have blessed me in so many ways. Protected me from side effects, kept my scans stable, placed wonderful people in my life. You have given me precious time. It's selfish, but I want more. I am not ready. I don't want to leave. Please, I just want more time.

Tears fell silently on my pillow until I fell asleep.

The next morning, we loaded the car. Kalea's friend Victoria was joining us. We settled in for the long drive, the kids lost in a sea of pillows and blankets in the back seat.

"You should sleep too," Mike said, reaching his hand over and resting it on my knee. I was exhausted but not sure I could sleep. My eyes were heavy but my heart was too, breaking like a crack in an iced-over pond. Slowly growing before a rush of fractures spread out and the unfortunate soul standing in the middle fell in, swallowed by the water.

The unfortunate soul was me.

An hour or so into the trip, I surrendered to the exhaustion and dozed off until I felt vibration under my feet. My phone was in my purse on the floor. It was Dr. Mendez's office. It was still early.

"Hi, Jen," said Julie. "The lab called. Your tumor markers are back down to your normal range. Still slightly elevated, but back to the normal range for you."

I heard what she said, but it didn't make sense.

I gave Mike a thumbs up as I listened to the nurse. With a big exhale, his shoulders dropped and his head fell back against the headrest, his body visibly releasing the fear of the last 18 hours.

"What?" I asked. "How can that be?"

"I have no explanation," she said, hearing the disbelief in her voice. "This never happens. Maybe it was a fluke? We can't really explain it."

I could. That was God. Divine Intervention. Answered prayer.

I already planned my upcoming week. I prepared to see the doctor, assuming he would schedule scans the following week. I dreaded having that conversation with my kids, my mom, and my friends, but I didn't have to do any of that now.

I squeezed Mike's hand. We smiled but couldn't scream. The kids were in the backseat, listening to music and playing on their phones. Blissfully unaware.

I leaned back in my seat, in awe of God's Grace and Mercy. So thankful to be the recipient of a God-breathed miracle on an ordinary Friday morning.

A while later, I checked our bank account, thinking of the extra dinners out and fun activities that always cost more than we planned. Our tax refund was deposited into our account that day though not expected for another week. God really did have a sense of humor.

Go celebrate, He said.

When we made it to Ocean City, I walked on the balcony and looked out at the ocean. It was cloudy, and I couldn't see the horizon. The next morning, fog covered my view of the sunrise. Normally, I would have been disappointed, but not this time.

I believed in things I couldn't see. I believed God walked with me through everything I had been through. He knew my path before I did. He put things in place right when I needed them. I didn't have to see it. I just had to have faith. Later the sun burned off that fog, the sky was bright blue, and the ocean stretched before me as far as I could see. It was there the whole time. Sometimes life got in the way and blocked my view. Even in the fog, I knew my blue sky was coming.

Chapter Forty-Three

I sat on the bed in my open-backed gown and hospital knee socks. As I waited for surgery, Mike searched on his phone to see if a guinea pig could be neutered. We bought two female guinea pigs from the pet store, but Kade announced there were baby guinea pigs in the cage that morning. On the same day I was having my reproductive organs removed, we became the proud parents of five guinea pigs.

I got the kids off to the bus stop and made myself a cup of tea. Still a little shaken from the tumor marker scare, I sat in the morning room with my thoughts. The house was quiet and the early morning light broke through the darkness. The birds chirped outside, anxious to begin the day. I wrapped my hands around my mug and sat back in the chair.

"It's a new day," I said. "Thank you, Lord for waking me up today."

I watched the birds fly from tree to tree. A squirrel scurried up the trunk of a tree and jumped into the branches, disappearing into the treetops. I was learning once again to live in the moment. I had a busy day ahead of me but right now, I wanted to enjoy my cup of tea and the stillness of the morning. When my mind drifted off to the worries of the day, I took a sip of tea and brought myself back to the moment. I read my devotion, wrote a few lines in my journal, and prayed.

Lord, thank you for this day. Thank you for your mercies as they are new every morning. Help me enjoy today without worry for tomorrow. Help me see the beauty even when things are hard. Help me look for the light in the darkest of situations. Use me to bless others, lift spirits, and spread Your Word. Place me in the right places with the right people and guide me in Your Ways. I want to serve you by serving others. Please watch over my family and friends today, and comfort those who are grieving this morning.

I lost another friend to metastatic breast cancer over the weekend. I clicked on her profile and scrolled back to a happier time. I looked at pictures of her with long hair and a healthy glow, smiling big with friends and family. Life before cancer. I looked at her children. They lost their most comfortable lap and most captive audience. I saw a picture of her and her husband from years ago. He stood behind her, chin resting on her shoulder, his arms wrapped tightly around her waist. He was smiling as he held his whole world. It was a stark contrast to the picture next to her in a hospital bed, his arm carefully draped over her shoulders so as not to hurt her. His brave smile covering the knowledge he was about to lose her.

Watching other women with my disease decline and pass away never got easier, but it made me more determined to live my life well. Their story was not my story. Life twisted and turned and the bottom fell out sometimes. The last four years had been a bumpy ride, and I knew the road conditions weren't going to improve. Right now, the ride was smooth and I planned to enjoy it while I could. Storms loomed ahead, but the sky above me was blue with puffy-white- clouds. I didn't need to look ahead, only beside me and all around, take in the sights and sounds along the way through this in between.

* *

"I'll have the nurse call in the refill for Ibrance," said Dr. Sonja. "You already have your appointment for next month. I will see you next time."

"Ok, have a great day," I said and then turned to get my things.

"Oh, one more thing. The cancer center has a team for Relay for Life in June," she said. "You should join our team."

"Sounds like fun. How do I sign up?"

"Go to the website. Sign up there," she said as we walked together down the hallway.

Later that night, on a whim, I formed my own team: "Jen's Confetti Crew" and shared it on my social media pages. My brother's employer donated sunshine yellow t-shirts. I ordered a large yellow flag on which I wrote a long list of names of family and friends affected by cancer. Kalea and Kade would be there with their friends, Victoria and Isabella. They would take turns walking the track with the flag.

The day of the event, we sat together in the bleachers for the opening ceremony, in a sea of yellow shirts. *They were all here for me.* My emotions caught in my throat, humbled so many came out to support me.

Get it together, Jen. The opening ceremony hadn't even started yet.

On the track, children held signs that said, "One Year" all the way up to "Ten Years". I assumed the years were survivor years. Because I had metastatic breast cancer, I was not technically a *survivor.* That term was reserved for people who had survived cancer and beat it. I couldn't say that anymore.

"I don't know what to do. *Survivor* doesn't apply to me," I whispered to Susan who was sitting next to me. Susan took a deep breath.

"You *are* a survivor," she said firmly. As she leaned in, she looked directly into my eyes, "You're still here."

She was right. I was still here.

"It's been almost 7 years since my first diagnosis. 7 years!" I said.

"See!," said Susan, shaking her head in feigned annoyance. "Not a survivor? Get out of here."

As the ceremony began, we found out the number signs meant years of participation in the event. When we were called, we walked onto the track for our first lap. My feet were unsteady for the first few steps, but they soon cooperated. I confidently circled the track with my Confetti Crew and began the day with my family and friends.

"We ask that all survivors meet at the high school for this evening's survivor dinner," the announcer said over the loudspeaker later that evening. There was that word again. *Survivor.*

Mike and I found seats on the balcony next to a lovely older couple. We talked a little bit about cancer and a bunch about baseball. From the balcony, I saw the field, the tent, and all the people. They were all affected by cancer in some way. There were so many. As dinner wrapped up, the volunteers walked us downstairs to the tunnel for the "Survivor Lap".

Standing next to the field, it looked like everyone left. The booths and the field were empty. I realized all the people were lined up inside of the track. So many people. The music started, and we walked onto the track. The lighthearted buzz that filled the place earlier in the day turned serious.

The crowd of friends had come and gone, but my family stood at the edge of the track, a small but energetic tribe in their sunshine shirts. They clapped, and cheered. Kade waved that big yellow flag back and forth as hard as he could, those names swaying in the breeze.

Earlier that morning, I debated if I was truly a *survivor*. I wondered no longer. As we rounded the last corner of the track, the crowd grew bigger and the cheers grew louder. I finally felt like I earned that title.

Survivor.

* *

I filled my pill box with my prescriptions and vitamins like I did every month. I erased last month's cycle number from the top left corner and wrote "47". I was about to start my 47th cycle of Ibrance, my first line of treatment. When I started Ibrance, another patient told me to expect about nine months of progression-free survival. The most I could hope for was about two years, and only if I tolerated the side effects. I got 47 more months!

It was a lazy summer morning when I left for my monthly appointment with Dr. Mendez. I set the batch of chocolate chip cookies I baked for the staff on the passenger seat and drove down Route 19 toward the cancer center. I wondered how many times I had taken that elevator as I rode up to the fifth floor, but the doors opened before I finished my calculations.

"Are those chocolate chip cookies?" asked one of the nurses as I set down the pan.

"Yes, they are," I said, "Enjoy!"

"Oh, we will," she said as she rushed off down the hall. "Thank you!"

I checked in and sat down across from a woman in a wheelchair wearing a scarf. She filled out paperwork on a clipboard while two women sitting next to her chatted and carried on.

"You guys are distracting me. Settle down. I got like 10 pages to fill out here," she joked with them.

"You better get busy then," one friend said and the two went back to chatting.

"I've had about enough of you two today," the woman in the wheelchair said. "I should have left you at home."

"We would have caught up to you," one said. "You can't roll that thing fast enough to lose us." They all laughed. I couldn't help but smile. They reminded me of the *Mom Squad*.

"Jennifer!" the nurse called as she opened the door, my file in her hand.

"No blood work today, right?" she asked.

"Right," I answered, following her to the first exam room. "I had bloodwork at the hospital last week with my scans."

I jumped on the scale and was pleased I lost another 3 pounds since the last visit. My blood pressure was normal. It used to be high when I came here. Back when that road was still unfamiliar, maybe? The nurse opened my file, and began to ask the usual questions.

"Same medications and supplements?"

"Yes," I said.

"Any falls since your last visit?"

"No. To everything," I said. "I haven't fallen. I don't have trouble swallowing. I can take care of myself. I have no new medications. No new symptoms..."

The nurse laughed. "You know the drill, I guess."

"Yes, I have done this a time or two," I said.

"Dr. Mendez will be in shortly. You take care."

I settled into the chair and welcomed the silence until I heard Dr. Mendez's familiar footsteps and quick knock at the door.

"Hey, Jen!" he said with that warm smile as the lights turned on. "So good to see you!" He put his arms out and I stood to give him a hug.

"So how about these scans?" he said, his smile grew bigger. "This is great! I love it! Right where we want to be."

"I hope it stays like this for a long time," I said.

"I am so pleased," he said. "Good scans. Tolerating the side effects. You are my rockstar."

Dr. Mendez looked through the chart, then motioned for me to hop up on the table. "You have been at this for a long time."

"I just started my 47th round of Ibrance," I told him as he listened to my heart and lungs.

"Yes, I was looking at that when I got your scan reports," he said, sitting down to flip through the pages of my file.

"It will be seven years since my first diagnosis in August," I announced. Dr. Mendez stopped flipping. He was quiet for a moment and then closed the file.

"You know as doctors, we are supposed to be very pragmatic and professional. Not get too involved. We can't predict the future, but we really root for you, Jen."

"Thank you," I said. "I wish you could...predict the future, I mean. I am always happy to get a stable scan. Since I have been on Ibrance for so long, I worry my time has to be running out."

"The trial came out a couple years before you started it. There are some patients still on it from that first trial so there are women on this protocol for over five years," he said.

"I want more than that," I said. "Way more than that."

"I want that too. You showed those doctors. Remember they told you—"

"That I'd be dead by now," I interrupted.

"Yes! Well, you know what you can tell them today," he said. "They didn't know what they were talking about."

"I'm still here," I said. "Take that!"

"Exactly. I'm so happy for you."

He closed my chart and we left the room. Like he did with all his patients, Dr. Mendez put his arm around my shoulder and walked me down the hall to the back waiting area.

"Jen, I want you to see your kids graduate, go off to college, and get married... and one day meet your grandkids."

"I want that too," I said, my voice cracking with unexpected emotion.

"I want it to be 2025 and you still on this first line of treatment," he said. "Just keep doing what you are doing and hold on to that hope."

There it was again. *Hope.*

"I will," I said. When we got to the waiting area, Dr. Mendez gave me another hug.

"Take a seat and we will get you out of here," he said. "We will see you next time." I sat in the chair against the wall and pulled out my phone to text Mike.

"All is well. Dr. Mendez said I'm a rockstar. Lol. Talk later. Love you." Mike was out of town and had meetings all day. He asked me to text him when I was finished.

On my way out, I held the door for a frail woman wearing a yellow scarf and pushed the call button on the elevator. I walked through the busy lobby, and waved to the desk clerk. The sliding doors opened to a warm summer day.

Breathing in the fresh air, I closed my eyes and felt the sun on my face. A blue sky with puffy-white-clouds hung in the heavens, the same as when I first learned I had cancer. I didn't understand how something so beautiful could be present on such a terrible day. Now I knew that life wasn't just good or bad. It wasn't storm clouds or rainbows. It was all those things, all at once. Instead of letting the darkness swallow me whole, I had to look for the light. It wasn't always easy to find but it was there. It was all over, really, in the in-between. I found it in places like sunsets and fresh flowers. I found it in books and mugs of hot tea.

And chocolate chip cookies.

Soft Chocolate Chip Cookies

Ingredients:

4 ½ to 5 Cups of All-Purpose Flour
2 teaspoons Baking Soda
2 Cups Butter, softened
1 ½ Cups Dark Brown Sugar
½ Cup White Sugar
2 x (3.4 ounces) Packages of Instant Vanilla Pudding mix
4 Eggs, Room Temperature
2 teaspoons Vanilla Extract
2 x (12 ounce) Bags of Chocolate Chips

Directions:

Preheat the oven to 350°.
Cream butter and sugars.
Add vanilla pudding and mix until blended.
Add eggs, one at a time, and then add vanilla.
Blend in the 4 ½ cups of flour and baking soda Add up to ½ cup of flour, if needed.Stir in the chocolate chips.
Use a medium cookie scoop and drop onto ungreased cookie sheets.
Bake for 9 to 12 minutes in the preheated oven until the edges are golden brown. Do not overbake.

"I dare you to take off the mask of perfection and show up as you are. Feel the freedom, the relief, the lightness. Because when we are real, that's when we actually heal. And those around us just might heal, too."
ASHLEY HETHERINGON

EPILOGUE

I just filled my pill box with my 56th round of Ibrance. My last scans were stable. Stable scans don't mean that I don't have cancer. The cancer cells are still working to take me down. I will never be done with treatment. I will never 'beat it'.

Scan. Treat. Repeat. Until I die.

People don't die from early stage breast cancer, only metastatic breast cancer One-hundred-and-sixteen women (and men) every day from MBC in the United States alone. There is no cure for metastatic breast cancer. Until more funding goes into research for metastatic disease, there won't be. You know those pink campaigns that raise awareness and pink washed products on the grocery store shelves? Those pink soup labels don't help me. I'm still dying. When October comes around and everything turns pink, be aware of where your money is going. Make your donation dollars count.

Stage IV needs more. Desperately.

I have a terminal disease but I still have an absolutely amazing life. It really is about perspective. I am still married to Superman, have the best mom, and two awesome kids. My friends are the sprinkles on top, or maybe the chocolate chips. I still hang out in my morning room and talk to God while I drink my tea and look out my window. Even on my hard days, I try not to complain.

Life is good.

My faith, my family, and my friends brought me through the darkest times in my life and will see me through what lies ahead. My time on this earth may be shorter than I imagined, but I will squeeze out every last drop while I am here. No bucket list required.

I wrote this book to tell my story and to share the lessons I learned. I want you to stop wasting time and start focusing on the right things. The good things. I want you to take notice of all the beauty in this world, even when it is hard to find. I promise. It's still there.

I'm not saying it is always easy. Life is hard sometimes. The storms, they will come. The skies will grow dark and the wind will knock you off your feet, but hold on. Have faith. Get up, dust yourself off, and keep going. The storm will pass and the sun will come out again.

But you know you have to look up to see it.

Really, look up. It's a blue sky with puffy-white-clouds.

My favorite.

Resources

Learn more about metastatic breast cancer

Metastatic Breast Cancer Network *mbcn.org*

Donate to research for metastatic breast cancer

Metavivor, *www.metavivor.org*

Charities that make a difference

Little Pink Houses of Hope, *www.littlepink.org*

Leslie's Week, *www.lesliesweek.org*

Inheritance of Hope, *inheritanceofhope.org*

About the Author

Jennifer Lilley Collins chases sunsets, bakes the best chocolate chip cookies, and believes a cup of hot tea soothes the soul. Jennifer's husband is named Mike, but she calls him Superman. They live near Pittsburgh, Pennsylvania with their two awesome kids, Kalea and Kade, her mom, and a Doberman named Moose.

In her former life, Jennifer spent a ridiculous amount of hours working on her business. Now, fighting metastatic breast cancer is her full-time job, but she makes time for reading, writing, and hanging out with her amazing friends as well as her oncologist. The In-Between is Everything is Jennifer's debut memoir. More information and her blog can be found at *www.lifeconfetti.blog.*